28 DAYS TO CHANGE YOUR LIFE

✷

Practical steps to mastering health, confidence
and personal success

Rachael Horton

CHANGE-4-LIFE UK LTD

Published in 2012 by Change-4-Life UK Ltd
The Comptons, Horsham,
West Sussex, RH13 5DW, United Kingdom

ISBN 978-0-9572419-0-9

www.change-4-life.com

CONTENTS

Daily Task Summary

	Day	Activity	Page
1 - Stress Busting	1	1-minute breathe in calm	24
	2	Taking control of your thoughts	28
	3	How to become more mindful	31
	4	How to think positive	36
	5	5-minute power relax	41
	6	Sleep enhancing techniques	50
	7	Visualising your new stress-free life	54
2 - Enhancing Body Health	1	Keep active	74
	2	Think your body fit and healthy	78
	3	Assessing hunger guide	83
	4	Motivate yourself to make healthy food choices	90
	5	Your powerful guide to eating with control	95
	6	Reset your full signal	100
	7	How to hydrate	106
3 - Projecting Confidence	1	Recognising the positive you	121
	2	Who is the ideal you?	125
	3	Standing tall and walking with confidence	129
	4	Speaking with confidence	132
	5	Think yourself assertive	136
	6	Instant assertiveness	141
	7	Perfect appearance	144

Daily Task Summary

	Day	Activity	Page
4 - Achieving Social Success	1	Think yourself socially successful	155
	2	Listen effectively	158
	3	Successful conversations (parts 1 & 2)	162 & 164
	4	Mindful interactions	167
	5	Instant rapport	171
	6	Social confidence	175
	7	Back to the start	178

This book is for you if ...

- You want to improve your health, confidence and relationships but have a hectic lifestyle.

- You often feel stressed and want some easy solutions to help you relax.

- You know much of the theory of healthy living but haven't got around to putting it into practice.

- You would like to think more positively and develop a positive mindset.

- You want to improve your motivation to take care of your body and become fitter and healthier.

- Your self-esteem and body image could do with a boost.

- You want to improve your relationships with others – either personal or professional.

28 Days to Change Your Life is about

The thoughts you have and the way you think influence your daily life more that you realise. By altering your thoughts, you can take control of your mind to make powerful (and long-term) improvements to many aspects of your life.

28 Days to Change Your Life is ...

A completely safe and natural way to lead a happier and healthier life. In the next 28 days my aim is to inspire you not only to live the life you choose, but to actually get you living it! The programme is designed for busy people in mind so it's easy to fit into even the most hectic schedule.

If this sounds like something that would change your life, then turn to the next page to find out how to get started.

WELCOME

✳

Introducing the New You

Living the dream: Your new start

Over the next 28 days, I would you like you to look upon me as your personal therapist – an experienced and encouraging voice that guides you through the pages of your book.

My aim is to give you tools that empower <u>you</u> to live a healthier, happier and more productive life, even if you have a hectic schedule! By the end of this journey, not only will you have a toolbox filled with simple, yet powerful, proven techniques, but you will also be experienced at using them. These proven tools have been tried and tested both by myself and my clients over the many years I have been practising as a qualified hypnotherapist. They work well not just in a therapy session but as part of everyday life, and I will be sharing these with you. I am also a scientist so I will explain not only how each tool works, but the reason it is a good addition to your overall toolbox.

The mind is a powerful thing

In the next 28 days you will be making incredible changes to your life using just one thing – the power of your own mind! Let me reassure you these techniques are completely safe, and natural, yet very powerful. If you follow them you will find that you quickly achieve success in four fundamental areas of your life which include stress reduction, health, confidence and successful relationships.

Our first meeting

I am very passionate about helping people, which I believe emanates from this book. Seeing clients make positive and lasting changes in their lives really is the most rewarding thing in the world for me.

All my clients are very important to me and whilst I may not have met you face-to-face, your success is equally as important. So consider this introduction a warm smile and gentle handshake as I welcome you to this new approach.

Why this book is different?

The difference with my book is that I bring the text to life by combining theory with daily practical activities – just as I would if you attended a therapy session with me. This is designed to give you not only the knowledge and inspiration to make changes, but actually get you living these changes. And before you know it, these new ways will become part of your everyday life, helping you when you need them most.

Small steps, big results

Most clients are a little nervous at their first session as they're not quite sure what to expect. Let me put you at ease by telling you that my approach is simple. It takes little time and yet gets big results. It involves making just one small achievable change each day that you will integrate easily into your lifestyle.

Our regular appointment

Each day I will provide you with one new tool to add to your toolbox – a new source of wisdom aimed to get you feeling good about yourself and back in control. I appreciate with a busy lifestyle it can be a challenge to set aside time to read the activities. So I designed the book to be read over breakfast, with you then putting the techniques into practice during your busy day. However, if reading over breakfast doesn't work for you, then simply set aside a regular time each day that fits into your lifestyle.

Why 28 days?

There are four common areas I am regularly asked to support clients with. Achieving success in each of these areas involves developing a number of skills. In my experience most people find this easier and more motivating when they practice a new skill each day. For this reason we will spend seven days learning a new skill each day in each of the four topic areas. This will give four 1-week chapters (28 days) supporting change.

What are the four areas?

I'll show you in the first week how to create a new stress-free way of life. Once you're enjoying feeling more calm, then in Week 2 we'll look at some easy techniques for improving health. To get your confidence soaring, Week 3 is packed with effective ways to boost your self-esteem so that by the final week you'll be ready to enjoy successful relationships with anyone you choose.

Minimum Effort, Maximum Effect: Your schedule

Here is your four-week schedule at a glance:

- *Chapter 1 Stress Busting*
    - o Essentials of a stress-free life.
    - o How to deal with every day stress, relax and think positively.

- *Chapter 2 Enhancing Body Health*
    - o Developing a healthy body and mind and becoming motivated to get fit.

- *Chapter 3 Projecting Confidence*
  - How to look and feel confident and create a positive self-image.

- *Chapter 4 Achieving Social Success*
  - Developing successful relationships with friends, family, colleagues or that someone special – even if you're still to meet!

A chapter summary at the end of each week is a useful reminder of your achievements. It's up to you whether you read the summary at the same time as the Day 7 activity, or simply read through it in the evening.

Tailor made for you

As we are all unique and learn in different ways, I've included a variety of different techniques so you can find things that work best for you. I will also ask you to reflect regularly on your achievements so you can feel good about how far you've come.

How to use this book

When writing this book, my intention was for you to work through it in order. However if you feel you would benefit from repeating a previous activity that's fine. Do whatever works best for you. If you are unable to complete a day for any reason, simply complete it when you are next able to do so. As long as you practice something each day, you will be making steps towards your new healthy, confident and stress-free life. Of course, you can always come back to the book any time to top-up these skills (or to revisit a specific activity)! You may like to set yourself reminders for the daily activities. Please complete just one day at a time. If you are unable to resist the temptation to read through the entire chapter first, please do return to Day 1 and complete the activities in order.

How successful you are at making the changes suggested in this book ultimately depends on how much you want to change, and the investment you make in practising your new skills. To get the most out of the practical tools, simply use them as part of your daily life. You'll see that some of the techniques need to be practiced and repeated until they become part of your daily life. With practice, you'll soon be leading the life you choose.

Overcoming challenges

From time-to-time we all encounter the occasional challenging day. It is important to keep motivated at these times as you can use them as valuable learning opportunities. They allow you to address old habits and prevent the cycle happening in the future. That way, even if your day doesn't start out quite as you'd hoped, you'll easily be able to turn it around. How we feel each day really is our choice and as we work together, I will show you how you can enjoy being at your best every day.

Preparing for your first session. Are you ready for this?

As with anything that changes your life as powerfully as this book, it is a good idea to chat with your doctor first to make sure this programme is suitable for you. Once you get the 'go ahead' then ask yourself *"How would life be if I was more relaxed, healthy, happy and confident?"* If you're ready to find out then prepare to turn to the next page as we begin our journey together.

CHAPTER ONE

*

Stress Busting

Hello and welcome to our first week together

I want to begin by saying 'Hello' and welcoming you to the first chapter of your new start. The next seven days are dedicated to helping you to let go of any stress and to feel calmer. The reason I've chosen to begin with stress busting is because it is one of the most common conditions clients ask me to help them with. In fact, people are so used to being tense that we have to begin with some instant *Stress Busting* techniques before we can even address the cause – or any other changes they want to make to their lives.

How will I help you to reduce stress?

To help my clients, I've developed a number of quick fix techniques for dealing with the fast pace of life. I will be sharing these with you during this week. We will also be exploring what causes *you* stress and how you can overcome it. I want you to feel reassured that we will be building up these techniques together slowly, taking it one step at a time. Very soon, you'll be able to recognise and stop that old feeling of worry before it even has chance to get started!

The stress effect

A little stress can be motivating and keep us on our toes. Think back to a time when you felt worried or even excited in the past. What did you notice? Perhaps your heart rate increased, you felt 'butterflies' in your stomach, or a feeling of being jittery or tense? For some, these feelings of being 'fired up' can motivate us to prepare well. For others, they dislike these feelings and want to avoid or run away from the situation. For this reason the stress reaction is often called the 'fight or flight response'.

How does stress affect *You*?

If you experience stress only occasionally it is a perfectly natural and harmless way for your body to look after you. However, if you suffer from stress and worry most days, it tends to become automatic, happening even though you don't want it to. This can lead to headaches, stomach troubles and even difficulty sleeping. You may even feel so stretched that the simplest thing 'winds you up' – even something trivial such as a slow moving queue in the supermarket.

How I can help

Whether you experience occasional stress or more frequent worry, fortunately I have many fast acting techniques that work well against stress. In fact, most clients report feeling much better (happier and more relaxed in previously stressful situations) even after the initial session with me. So let's start with a basic technique that requires small effort but gets big results – *breathing*.

Day 1: Breathe in calm

Today is all about breathing – *correctly*. Whilst breathing is something we all do several times a day, if you're under a lot of stress, it is one of the first things that can become affected. As this happens gradually you may be unaware that your breathing is shallow and fast. However, breathing in this way can leave you feeling more anxious and tense. I have a really simple solution to overcome this. It is designed to take just 1-minute to do. Before I reveal this technique, let's find out how you breathe now.

How am I currently breathing?

Good breathing technique is really important if you want to feel more relaxed. Take a moment to have a go at this simple test to find out if you're breathing correctly.

👍 CATCHING YOUR BREATH – CHECK YOUR BREATHING TECHNIQUE

I recommend that you try out this technique sitting down to begin with.

1 Place one hand on your chest and the other hand on your stomach.

2 Take a deep breath, then let it out.

3 Now simply observe your breathing come and go for a few breaths.

4 Ask yourself, "Which hand moved the most?"

If it was the hand on your stomach, then congratulations you probably have good technique and should continue to breathe in this good way. If it was the hand on your chest, then I'd like you to repeat *Catching Your Breath* but this time, concentrate on keeping your chest still so only the hand on your stomach moves. Let this happen comfortably and naturally. It does take a little practice but very quickly you will notice yourself breathing more and more in this good, deep, effective way. Make sure you can comfortably do this before you read on.

What are the benefits of better breathing?

Breathing in this way will help you to feel more alert and energised throughout the day. It keeps your body oxygenated allowing you to feel more motivated to make changes. You should also notice how you feel calmer in mind and body.

Back to (breathing) basics

Here is your 1-minute activity for today. I would recommend practising this again at least three times throughout the day. Perhaps in the middle of the morning, before lunch and again before you go to sleep. Practice it sitting down initially as you may feel a little dizzy from all the extra oxygen. This dizziness will quickly fade. Once you've mastered the technique, you can use it in meetings, when in a queue at the supermarket or even when you're on the phone. It's a simple, yet powerful way for you to begin your journey to a more relaxed life.

👆 **1-MINUTE BREATHE IN CALM**

1 Breathe in slowly through your nose (remembering to breathe from your stomach) for a count of 4.

2 Hold your breath for a count of 7.

3 Breathe out s-l-o-w-l-y through your mouth (as if gently blowing out a candle) for a count of 8.

4 Repeat the above five times. Then go about your day.

Using this technique, you should notice that your breathing becomes slower, and you start to release any tension. Let this happen comfortably and naturally. Very quickly this will become a reliable instant stress buster in your toolbox – and a breath of fresh air for your new stress free start.

Day 2: Identifying what causes you stress

Stress and the mind

Do you ever find that when you worry about something, you tend to think of the worst possible scenario – or even picture things going badly in your mind? Each time you do this, you will probably notice that you become even more stressed and anxious. If you want to stop that old stress response all you need to do is change the thoughts and pictures in your mind so they are of positive outcomes. Whilst this may be easier said than done, I'll take you through this step-by-step over the next few days.

Choosing your new response

For today, let's begin by finding out how you currently respond to stress. That way you'll be able to recognise those tell-tale signs. I also want you to think about how you would prefer to respond in the future. That way, you can choose the most appropriate response and really tailor this activity to meet your needs. This is a written task to begin with so you'll need a pen.

IDENTIFYING STRESSORS

Think back to an event or situation that caused you stress. Make a note of the event below. Think about your thoughts and emotions at the time, the potential cause or triggers, and how you responded (your actions or your emotions). Then choose how you would prefer to respond to similar events in the future. I've included an extra row in case you want to repeat the task with other situations.

What was the situation?	What were your thoughts & emotions?	What was the cause/ trigger(s)?	How did you respond?	How would you prefer to respond?
Identify the events or situations that caused you stress	• "I'm annoyed" • Impatient • Anxious	• Stressful situation? • Conflict with someone?	• Angry • Fearfully	How would you handle the situation differently?

Stress starts with a single thought

Take a moment to look over the thoughts and emotions you've written down. What are the tell-tale signs that your stress response is starting? The process is usually started by a thought – although because our thoughts tend to come and go very quickly, you may actually notice the emotion first. This might be a feeling of being anxious, annoyed or even overwhelmed perhaps?

A better way

Now take a moment to look at how you would prefer to respond to the situation in the future. Make sure this new response gives you a positive outcome. What positive thoughts do you need to have to get this response?

Later this week I will show you how to stop the old thoughts and replace them with your new more positive ones. As you start thinking in this better way, your responses will change for the better too.

Preparing to think positively

To help you prepare for thinking in a more helpful way, you need to become aware of how you think now. So your goal for today is simply to understand your thought processes in response to stress. As you do this, you can start to gain control of your mind and emotions. The secret to developing this ability is to become aware of what you're thinking and feeling moment-to-moment.

Here's my quick guide to developing your self-awareness and reducing stress.

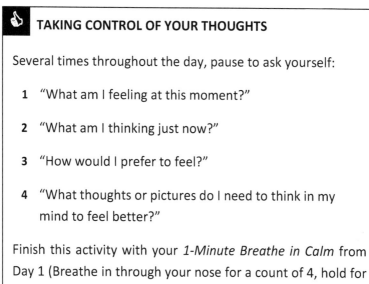

👍 TAKING CONTROL OF YOUR THOUGHTS

Several times throughout the day, pause to ask yourself:

1 "What am I feeling at this moment?"

2 "What am I thinking just now?"

3 "How would I prefer to feel?"

4 "What thoughts or pictures do I need to think in my mind to feel better?"

Finish this activity with your *1-Minute Breathe in Calm* from Day 1 (Breathe in through your nose for a count of 4, hold for 7, breathe out slowly for 8).

This activity should take no longer than a couple of minutes. Each time you do it you will be gaining more control over your thinking – a powerful start to changing your outlook and your life.

Day 3: Mindfulness, the pre-requisite for positive thinking

Change your mind(set), change your life

Have you ever found that you move from one thought or feeling to another very quickly? This is because the mind tends to jump from thought to thought unless it is brought under our control. You have the power to literally *change your mind* and choose how you want to feel. This is important as what you think about the mind magnifies.

Today you will begin to change your mindset for the better by becoming more aware of what you're thinking. First though, let's explore how your thinking is now.

Do you spend most your time in the past, the present or the future?

Many of us spend our lives thinking about the past – often what we should or shouldn't have said or done; or the future – what may or may not go wrong! If you tend to do this and want to become more positive, it can be helpful to practice being in 'the now'. That way you can enjoy being in the present moment rather than either worrying about things that you can't change in the past – or the worst case scenario, worrying about the future. This is also a good starting point to ease you into developing a positive outlook.

Previously, in Day 2 ...

We started the process of becoming aware of how you are thinking and feeling in the *Taking Control of Your Thoughts* activity. This was to help you begin to get control of your thoughts and what you were thinking at any moment. The ability to think and be aware of how you feel in the present moment is called mindfulness. If you're not accustomed to thinking in a positive way, becoming more mindful of your thought processes will help prepare you for the positive thinking techniques I will show you later this week.

Becoming more mindful

Today I will show you an easy way to become more mindful. Even better, this technique will take no extra time as you will do it during your normal daily activities. For added effect combine this with the *1-Minute Breathe in Calm* activity from earlier this week.

👍 **HOW TO BECOME MORE MINDFUL**

Throughout the day, take time to pay attention to your thoughts and the sensations in your body.

- To do this focus on *this second*, *this moment*, then the next. For instance, be aware of what's happening in the present – the sounds around you. Not judging, just noticing your surroundings.
- Become aware of your breathing too – of your lungs filling gently with air on the 'in' breath and emptying on the 'out' breath.
- Notice how your body feels. For instance, feel the sensation of the surface beneath you, or the movement or sensation in your muscles.
- Notice any thoughts. What are you thinking right now?
- How do you feel emotionally?

I find it useful to practice mindfulness during mealtimes or when I'm walking. Here are some easy ways to do this:

1 Mindful at mealtimes

- Each time you eat, take small bites and eat very s-l-o-w-l-y.
- Focus on the sensation of chewing your food and really savouring the flavours.

➡

---

2 Mindfulness when walking

- As you walk, become aware of each physical step you take.

- Feel the sensation of your feet gently touching the ground and the movement in your muscles.

- Notice the changes in your breathing as you move.

- Observe the temperature of the air or the sensation of the breeze against your face. Really enjoy being in the moment and savouring the atmosphere.

You are what you think

How you feel at any given moment depends on the thoughts you are thinking at that time. It's not easy to notice our thoughts as they tend to come and go very quickly. What is easier is to recognise how you're feeling. If you're feeling good then your thoughts are working well for you. If you're not feeling as good as you would like to, then giving yourself a 'pep talk' from time-to-time can be motivating. For those of you who would like some extra encouragement to think in a more positive way, try this *Motivational Self-Talk* activity. If you want to, you can tailor this to you by using some of your own inspiring phrases.

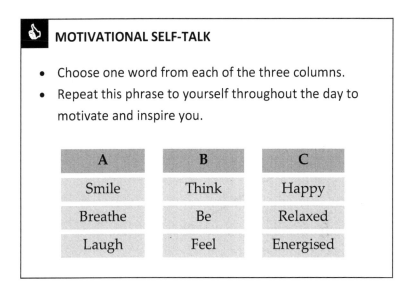

MOTIVATIONAL SELF-TALK

- Choose one word from each of the three columns.
- Repeat this phrase to yourself throughout the day to motivate and inspire you.

A	B	C
Smile	Think	Happy
Breathe	Be	Relaxed
Laugh	Feel	Energised

Get ready for positive thinking

The techniques I have shown you over the last three days are designed to get you to become aware of your thoughts. By doing this you can start to change your thinking for the better. This will help you to feel better in yourself and calmer in your daily life. So if you tend to think in a more *glass half empty* rather than a *glass half full* way, then this will prepare you well for Day 4, as I show you how to think positive.

Day 4: The power of positive thinking

Have you ever noticed how it's a joy to be around people who have an uplifting attitude? Their enthusiasm is infectious and makes us feel alive and positive. They also tend to attract people and opportunities to them with their inspiring outlook.

Would you like to think positively?

Even if you're already accustomed to thinking positively, you are likely to still get a lot of benefit from today's activity. Positive thinking is more than just 'looking on the bright side'. It's an entire outlook on life and may involve changing how you currently view some situations. The techniques I'll show you require commitment and dedication, as the mind can sometimes show some resistance along the way. However, I do recommend persevering as once you make positive thinking a habit, the world around you will begin to change for the better. Your new outlook will also help you through even the most challenging times and also act as a powerful antidote to stress.

Focus on what you want

If you try not to think about something, you will find that you tend to think about it more! An example is many of my weight loss clients before they first come to see me will say to themselves, "Don't think about food," and guess what happens? The mind doesn't register the word 'don't' and their focus becomes food and eating. The secret to positive thinking is to focus on what you want (the successful outcomes) rather than what you don't. To do this, your thoughts, the images in your mind, and the words you speak must be of the things you want. Whilst the occasional moan might seem like a stress reliever, over time such negative thoughts can take their toll.

Would you like to choose how you will feel throughout each day?

It really is possible to wake up each morning and choose to feel positive throughout the day. The more you do this, the more feeling good and thinking in a helpful way will become automatic for you until they eventually become your natural way of approaching every situation.

👍 HOW TO THINK POSITIVE

1 First thing each morning, begin by practising your *1-Minute Breathe in Calm* (breathe in through your nose for a count of 4, hold for 7, breathe out slowly for 8).

2 Think about how you would like to feel throughout the day (e.g. upbeat, positive, cheerful).

   • It may help you to remember a time when you felt especially good.

   • Let yourself feel that good feeling flow through your body until you feel happy and start to smile.

   • Visualise yourself exactly how you want to be, enjoying your day with everything going well.

3 *STOP.* Concentrate on your thoughts for a few moments. Be patient as this does take some practice. If any unhelpful thoughts or images enter your mind simply say 'STOP' to yourself, or imagine a 'STOP' sign.

4 *ERASE.* Imagine erasing any unhelpful thoughts or images.

5 *REPLACE.* Replace with alternative thoughts or images that are supportive, encouraging and helpful.

6 Throughout today, if you experience any old negative feelings or stress STOP-ERASE-REPLACE.

What makes you feel good?

Another way to train your mind to naturally switch to the positive, is to notice whenever you feel less than good and shift your thinking onto things that make you feel more positive. For instance uplifting thoughts of:

- being successful
- things you enjoy
- things you're looking forward to doing
- memories of happy times
- people you like.

Smile a winning smile

For me, I find having a genuine warm smile and a light-hearted approach to life makes me think and feel more positive. Smiling also encourages the body to produce 'feel good' hormones that reduce stress. So give smiling a try today – a genuine smile whenever you meet someone. By the end of the today if you've been practising your smile, thinking positively, and choosing how you will feel, stress will quickly become a thing of the past and feeling good will be your new future.

Note: The *Stop-Erase-Replace* technique may take a few weeks of practice to master fully. However, would you agree that a few moments of practice each day is worth a lifetime of feeling more positive and enjoying life much more?

Day 5: Power relax

Most clients in my therapy practice that have been suffering from stress tell me they can never relax – and yet they tend to experience the deepest levels of relaxation during the session! Taking time to stop and unwind is just as important as eating healthily and taking regular exercise. Yet how many of us take time out of our day to recharge our batteries?

Do you feel that you just don't have enough time in your day to stop and relax? However, if taking just 5 minutes each day will make you more productive, improve your health and help you to feel happier and more positive, wouldn't it be worth the investment in time?

Peace and quiet

If you're like me and tend to live in a fast-paced world surrounded by endless distractions, by finding just a few moments of peace you will begin to appreciate the value of quiet time for your health and wellbeing. It can be easier to find quiet when you're in nature appreciating the calm, whilst sitting on a tranquil beach or by the river listening to the wind in the trees. But if you're short on time finding even a few moments to spend less time *doing* and more time *being* is a valuable investment in your health and great stress buster!

Reducing your stress levels – fast!

Today I'm going to teach you a 5-minute power relaxation. If you set aside a minimum of 5 minutes each day to practice this technique, you'll begin to notice a dramatic reduction in your overall stress levels.

👍 **5-MINUTE POWER RELAX**

1 Lie down with a pillow beneath your head. Avoid lying in bed as you might fall asleep!

2 Now sit up, close your eyes and say to yourself the words,

- Relax, relax, relax, lax.

- As you say the word 'lax', allow your body to fall back onto your pillow with your eyes closed.

3 Spend a few minutes just relaxing.

- If your thoughts start to wander then simply bring your awareness to your breathing.

- If you want to relax even more deeply, then imagine a peaceful, tranquil place that you find relaxing such as a tropical beach or a meadow. Use all your senses to make the experience as vivid as you can. For example:

  o *See* the soft white sand and the glistening of the warm blue ocean.

  o *Hear* the sounds of the birds of paradise as they gently fly past.

  o *Feel* the comfortably warm temperature of the air, the grains of sand between your toes.

  o *Smell* the cool salty ocean.

  o *Taste* the salty breeze on your tongue.

Opening your eyes brings you instantly up and out of your power relaxation. Ready to enjoy a feeling of calm throughout the rest of your day.

Instant Reviver

Have you ever woken up in the morning only to find that you're still feeling exhausted and yet you have a full day ahead that you need to face? I can provide you with a technique you can use anytime to instantly revive you. This will help you to immediately recharge your batteries and get on with your day.

> 👍 **BATTERY RECHARGE**
>
> 1 Find a quiet place to sit down for a moment. It can be helpful to close your eyes if you are able to.
>
> 2 Take a few calming breaths using your *1-Minute Breathe in Calm* technique (breathe in through your nose for a count of 4, hold for 7, breathe out slowly for 8).
>
> 3 Imagine a battery symbol like that on a mobile phone. If yours looks a little 'flat' imagine it charging and allow the energy to fill your entire body, moving up from your toes, all the way up to the top of your head.
>
>   • It can be helpful to imagine a colour moving up with it, re-energising you.
>
> 4 Take a moment to enjoy feeling relaxed yet re-energised before opening your eyes and continuing with your day.

With regular practice of these techniques you will quickly start to notice how you are much calmer and relaxed in everyday life. You'll experience more success and happiness. Stress will start to become a thing of the past as you enjoy your new positive, relaxed lifestyle.

Day 6: Sound asleep

If you are suffering from stress you may, at times, have found it difficult to get to sleep or to stay asleep. It is also common for clients suffering from chronic stress to tell me they wake up early with their mind racing thinking through all the things they need to get done the following day. However, by the time morning comes around, they are so exhausted from not sleeping it can be difficult to be at their best. Fortunately I have many effective techniques to help with this.

Since a good night's sleep is so important to our health and wellbeing, and can affect how we feel, today you'll discover how to sleep better. Even if you regularly sleep well, the tips, hints and techniques I'll show you will help you enjoy a good rest every night. By learning to sleep well, you can reduce stress and enjoy feeling re-energised. In the meantime, if you need to, use the *Battery Recharge* technique from Day 5 to instantly revive and re-energise you.

The natural sleep cycle

The amount of sleep we need is unique to all of us. It varies with age and the amount of activity we've had during the day. Most people require between 6 and 10 hours. There are three main ways we can help ensure a good night's sleep:

1. Freeing ourselves from things that interfere with sleep.

2. Changing our lifestyle to improve sleep (including getting more exercise).

3. Learning techniques that encourage us to get to sleep, and stay asleep.

Eliminating sleep deprivers

Use this checklist to find out (and get rid of) anything that may be depriving you of sleep.

👆 HOW TO ELIMINATE SLEEP DEPRIVERS

1   *Smoking.* Cigarettes contain nicotine which is a stimulant. Becoming a non-smoker can aid a restful sleep. If you do smoke, avoid cigarettes at least 4 hours before you go to bed.

2   *Alcohol.* Affects our sleep quality so we sleep lighter and more restlessly. It is best to avoid alcohol if you have difficulty sleeping.

3   *Caffeine.* Is a stimulant found in coffee, tea, chocolate and some carbonated drinks. Some headache remedies also contain caffeine. Caffeine takes between 6 and 8 hours to leave our bodies. Therefore limit your intake and avoid caffeine after 3pm.

4   *Processed or refined foods.* These are often high in sugar and may over-stimulate the body. Instead opt for fresh natural foods that are more easily digested. Foods high in tryptophan (a chemical that helps calm the mind) may aid sleep. Examples include oats, poultry, sesame seeds and sunflower seeds. ➲

5 *Eating just before bed.* The body needs time to actively digest food and is more efficient and comfortable when we are upright. Therefore avoid eating too close to bedtime. However, avoid eating too early as being hungry can also keep you awake.

6 *Being overweight.* If you are overweight or obese you are more likely to experience sleep disturbances. Aim to maintain a healthy weight and take regular activity.

7 *Stress and worry.* Making time to practice relaxation (*1-Minute Breathe in Calm*, Day 1; *5-Minute Power Relax*, Day 5) and letting go of stress and worry can help improve your mood and reduce the tendency to wake early in the morning. These techniques can also be used to help you get to sleep, or to get back to sleep easily if you awake in the middle of the night.

Lifestyle changes to improve sleep

Use this checklist to make any positive lifestyle changes to encourage a good sleep night after night.

☜ HOW TO MAKE LIFESTYLE CHANGES THAT IMPROVE SLEEP

1 *Regular physical activity.* Helps reduce stress hormones and boost confidence. Even a 15 minute brisk walk each day will make a difference. Although avoid exercising a few hours before bed.

2 *Relaxation techniques.* Make time each day to practice your *1-Minute Breathe in Calm* (Day 1), and *5-Minute Power Relax* (Day 5) to relax your mind and body.

3 *Unwind from your day.* Here are some ways to help you unwind from your day:

- *Step outside and take 3 deep relaxing breaths.* As you breathe out, let any tension you feel in your body simply dissolve away. Then become mindful of the refreshing air, the temperature, the world going on around you.

- *Prepare a 'to do list' in plenty of time before bed.* This will help prevent you thinking about all the tasks you have to get done. Thinking back through your day can help your mind to process events from the day and help you to relax. ➲

4   *Establish a bedtime routine.* A pre-sleep routine signals to our body that it's time to wind down ready to sleep. A warm bath, listening to relaxing music, or reading a book before getting into bed are simple ways to calm your mind and body. Here are some other tips:

- *Only go to bed when you are sleepy.* Even if this means that you stay up slightly later than usual. Avoid taking naps or 'sleeping in' to catch-up on sleep. If you need to 'sleep in' at the weekend, limit this to no more than around an hour later than your usual getting up time. Get up at the same time each day.

- *Avoid watching TV just before going to bed.* Switch off the TV, games consoles, your computer and mobile phone and establish a relaxing bedtime routine.

5   *Bedroom environment.* Make sure your bed is warm in a suitably cool room. The bed, mattress and pillows should be comfortable and the room dark and quiet. You can listen to relaxing natural sounds such as waves or waterfalls, or use ear plugs, to distract from any background noise. Avoid watching TV, eating, reading or talking on the phone whilst in bed, so that your mind associates bed simply with sleeping.

Techniques for improving sleep

Now that you have eliminated the main culprits responsible for poor sleep, you should start to notice your sleep improving. Use the tips below if ever you have difficulty getting to sleep.

👍 **SLEEP ENHANCING TECHNIQUES**

1 *Get up if you're awake for more than 30 minutes.* Have a milky drink (not hot chocolate), listen to relaxing music, read a relaxing book or do something restful until you start to feel sleepy.

2 *Avoid looking at the clock.* Continually opening your eyes will wake you further.

3 *Keep a pen and paper by your bed.* If you have things on your mind that you need to remember, writing them down can help you to relax. That way you know that you can deal with them the next day.

4 *Think positive thoughts.* Make sure your thoughts are helpful. If you're thinking "I'll never get to sleep," or "I must sleep or I'll be exhausted tomorrow," you are less likely to get to sleep. Instead practice the *How to Think Positive* (Day 4) activity to Stop-Erase-Replace any unhelpful thoughts with supportive, encouraging alternatives.

➡

- Remember lying in bed feeling relaxed can be just as refreshing as sleep. Use the time to daydream about something pleasant, such as relaxing on a tropical beach. Really enjoy the experience.

5 *Follow your thoughts.* Make your inner voice slow and sound tired, like a bedtime story, as you follow your thoughts. You should quickly notice how you feel sleepy.

6 *Focus on what you want.* Concentrate on what it's like to be asleep. Focus on that dreamy state. You can even combine this with calm breathing (*1-Minute Breathe in Calm,* Day 1), as well as your power relaxation (*5-Minute Power Relax,* Day 5).

While you are making positive lifestyle changes that encourage a refreshing sleep you must be patient. Resetting your sleep cycle does take a little time. However, you should quickly begin to notice your sleep improves and night after night your sleep just gets better and better.

Day 7: Your personal vision of the future

Your new story

During this week we have focused on mental wellness – listening to the mind's signals. In Chapter 2 we will focus on physical wellness – listening to the body's signals and how it is feeling. As the body responds to what the mind focuses on, today you will create, and mentally rehearse, your new stress free life. That way your body can re-learn what relaxation is.

Directing your own mental movie

Many successful business entrepreneurs and sports professionals use a powerful technique called visualisation to achieve what they want. It's actually quite easy to do and best of all anyone can do it. To successfully change your mindset using visualisation, the secret is to focus on what you want and use all your senses to really enjoy the experience.

This technique even works for people who don't think they are very imaginative or creative. Simply take it step-by-step so you imagine changing just one thing in your life at a time. During your mental movie you will get to be the director and will mentally rehearse your new future exactly as you want it to be and at a pace that's right for you.

Rehearsing your new relaxed future

The more you mentally rehearse what you want, the more your mind will achieve it. Your physical responses and behaviours will automatically start to change for the better too. For instance, if you visualise and really imagine yourself feeling calm and relaxed in previously stressful situations, your body will automatically know to feel more calm and comfortable when you are actually in those situations.

The right direction

As we prepare for today's activity it's time to make yourself comfortable. Set yourself up for your new start by taking three calming breaths using the *1-Minute Breathe in Calm* technique from Day 1 (Breathe in through your nose for a count of 4, hold for 7, breathe out slowly for 8) followed by the *5-Minute Power Relax* from Day 5.

Are you ready to experience your new direction, your new relaxed life? Once you're ready, let's get started.

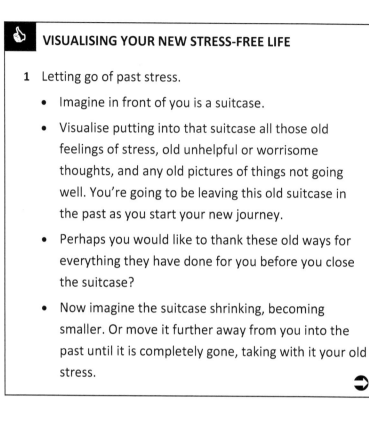

VISUALISING YOUR NEW STRESS-FREE LIFE

1 Letting go of past stress.

   - Imagine in front of you is a suitcase.

   - Visualise putting into that suitcase all those old feelings of stress, old unhelpful or worrisome thoughts, and any old pictures of things not going well. You're going to be leaving this old suitcase in the past as you start your new journey.

   - Perhaps you would like to thank these old ways for everything they have done for you before you close the suitcase?

   - Now imagine the suitcase shrinking, becoming smaller. Or move it further away from you into the past until it is completely gone, taking with it your old stress.

2 Your new relaxed future.

- Picture a new journey unfolding ahead of you as you travel into a relaxed, stress-free future.

- Take this step-by-step, thinking of the next 24 hours rehearsing what you want.

- Be in the picture and see yourself exactly as you want to be:

  o approaching everything in a positive way

  o feeling calm throughout the day

  o keeping positive, cheerful and light-hearted

  o having successful interactions with others

  o feeling healthy and taking good care of yourself

  o taking time to do something you enjoy.

- Notice the thoughts of the new relaxed you:

  o your inner voice is positive, supportive, encouraging

  o your thoughts are helpful, happy.

Note: It is very important that you visualise your day going well and that you are calm throughout. If any unhelpful thoughts or images should enter your mind, STOP-ERASE-REPLACE them with helpful alternatives (*How to Think Positive*, Day 4).

➲

If you still experience any apprehension after doing this, imagine watching this new future as if it is happening to someone else. Watch their perfect performance and when you feel comfortable, imagine stepping back into the story so you can see, feel and hear everything going perfectly. Remember to use all your senses to make the experience as vivid as possible. By doing this you will be training your mind to respond in this new way.

3 When you're ready, let your body stretch, open your eyes and enjoy living out your new stress-free life, as you did during the visualisation.

Living your ideal future

The human mind has a tremendous capacity to create a bright new future for you. As you become experienced at picturing your ideal future, you can travel further forwards in time, perhaps to one week from now. Each time you do this, notice all the changes to how you're looking and feeling as you enjoy your new relaxed lifestyle.

Every time you practice this you are changing your thoughts for the better. You can adapt and refine the images and feelings until they are exactly what you want. However, the real icing on the cake is to be able to travel forwards several months or years in your successful future and then work back to see all the individual changes you need to make to achieve success. This will give you a clear vision of what you need to do. As your old stress and worries dissolve away and become a thing of the past, you can look forward to your new relaxed and happy future.

CHAPTER 1 SUMMARY

Noticing change

This week I have given you a glimpse of what a stress-free life is like. As we come towards the end of our first week, you should be noticing either a feeling of being calmer and more in control, or at least that you have some techniques you can rely on to help you feel better. It is quite common for people around you to notice the changes you're making before you do.

Taking a moment to reflect on all the things you have learned this week and any positive benefits is a valuable way to help you progress and feel good. I've prepared a summary to help you as you do this:

- *Being relaxed begins in the mind.* You can become more relaxed simply by changing how you view and respond to situations. By becoming aware and letting go of past stressful ways you can create a more relaxed future.

- *Your mind controls your body.* Every heartbeat, every breath, every thought, every emotion is controlled by the mind. If you want to get control of the physical effects of stress, it starts with controlling the mind.

- *Make being relaxed part of your lifestyle.* Daily practice of the stress busting techniques in this chapter takes minimal time and can easily be made part of your normal day, making it possible to lead a busy life and still be relaxed.

- *Start your day with calm breathing (from your stomach).* Correct breathing will energise and calm your mind for the day.

- *How you feel in your mind affects how you feel in your body.* A daily five minute relaxation quietens the mind and relaxes the body.

- *Focus on what you want.* The mind gravitates towards what you think about most. How you feel depends on the thoughts you have. You can take control of your thoughts by thinking about and picturing what you want (successful outcomes).

- *Be mindful.* Enjoying the present helps you become aware of your thoughts so you can choose how you respond to any situation.

- *Create a positive outlook.* A positive outlook helps you deal calmly and comfortably with even the most challenging situations.

- *STOP-ERASE-REPLACE old stress.* Recognise when you are becoming stressed or worried and replace unhelpful thoughts with positive alternatives.

- *Smile.* It makes you feel good and brightens up the lives of others too.

- *Lead a healthy balanced lifestyle to aid restful sleep.* A healthy balanced life with a relaxing sleep routine prepares the mind for a good sleep to repair and rejuvenate.

- *Act the person you aspire to be.* Daily visualisation programmes your mind to become exactly as you want to be. Remember to use all your senses to make the experience as vivid and compelling as you can.

How to get these techniques to work for you

If you really want to get the best from these techniques, I recommend making them part of your daily lifestyle. That way you are likely to find yourself carrying them out without even thinking about it! To help you, I will share with you how I fit all these stress busting activities into my day. Of course, as everyone's daily schedule is different, it's important to find what works best for you.

How I integrate the stress busting techniques into my busy lifestyle

I start my day with the 1-Minute Breathe in Calm.

I prefer to do this before I get out of bed in the morning. A couple of rounds of breathing set me up for a calm start to the day. I sometimes combine this with motivating self-talk.

Over breakfast is a great opportunity to be mindful.

I become aware of what I'm eating, really enjoying savouring every mouthful and tasting the flavours. It doesn't take up any extra time and I've found that I enjoy food more, and eat less too! In the next chapter I'll show how you can use mindfulness at mealtimes to get control over your eating. It's an easy way to maintain a healthy body weight.

If I notice I'm not feeling as good as I could be, I 'catch my thoughts'.

During my busy day if I notice I'm starting to feel stressed, I consciously 'catch' my thoughts. When I first started doing this I found that I was thinking about worst case scenarios that usually didn't happen. So now I simply replace these thoughts with something better. I usually end up smiling to myself at how funny my old thoughts had been. With a little practice, I am now much more in tune with my emotions too. If I find myself getting annoyed or frustrated about something, I take a moment to think about what's really bothering me. Then I decide how I prefer to respond.

I find a friendly genuine smile helps me feel good and doesn't take up any time.

This makes me feel happy and brightens up the day of others – whether people in my local supermarket or my colleagues and friends.

When I get home from my day I spend 5 minutes relaxing.

This helps me to 'switch off' from my day and gets me ready for a relaxing evening. I find that if I do this as soon as I get in, it prevents me from being side-tracked to do other things. It only takes a few minutes and I use this time to visualise how I want to think and feel the following day.

My bedroom is a haven I can retreat to at the end of the day.

I look forward to a relaxing sleep each night. I eat a healthy balance of fresh foods, including those that enhance sleep, and I avoid caffeine after lunch. I prepare my mind for sleep by switching off the TV early and getting a warm bath or reading a good book. I'm quite accustomed now to taking myself from wakefulness into a wonderful relaxing sleep. On the rare occasion I need to quieten my mind, I use the *1-Minute Breathe in Calm* technique and then allow my thoughts to become drowsy. I actually imagine what it's like to drift to sleep and that's usually the last thing I remember until the next morning when I awake refreshed and energised for my day.

Being relaxed and stress free is ultimately down to each of us and how we choose to live our lives. Make relaxation your new choice and enjoy feeling happier.

CHAPTER TWO

*

Enhancing Body Health

Welcome to Week 2

How healthy are you?

When we're busy or stressed we often neglect the most important thing – our body. For me, I often used to find that if I was tired or overworked healthy eating, regular exercise and adequate rest would go out the window – just at a time when I needed them most!

In this week, I'll guide you through a selection of short daily activities that will help you to optimise your body health. Similar to last week, these are designed to fit easily into your lifestyle no matter how busy you are.

Think yourself healthy

In the first week I gave you a flavour of how to use the power of your mind to let go of stress. Listening to your mind's signals and becoming more in tune with your thinking and emotions is the first step towards optimising health. However, if you haven't been giving your body the attention it deserves, then this week I'll show you how to become aware of what it needs. I will be sharing with you some practical ways you can powerfully change your mind towards optimum body health.

What do you want to achieve for your health?

Before I reveal how to become fitter, eat healthily and with control, or even maintain a healthy body weight, I would like you to ask yourself the following two questions and note down your answers in the box below. That way you can review your progress at the end of the week.

✏️ DECIDING WHAT YOU NEED TO CHANGE

What do you want to change to improve your health?	How will making this change improve your life?

When I ask my clients these questions, they often tell me they wish they had more control over their eating, they want the motivation to stay fit and that they need to drink more water. We will cover all of these things this week as I show you how to easily fit healthy behaviours into your busy life.

This activity will help you to identify all the benefits to you of improving your health. By doing this, and focusing on what you want, it will help motivate and inspire you towards your goal.

Now you have explored what you personally need to do to improve your health, are you ready to find out how to be fit, energised and motivated to eat healthily and with control? If so, read on as I have the answer ...

Day 1: Small steps to a fitter body

How can you fit extra activity into your already busy lifestyle?

Do you ever find yourself taking the car a short distance when you know you could walk? Or taking the lift instead of the stairs? And when did you last spend a day simply enjoying being outdoors? My clients often tell me that they don't have time to exercise. They are so busy with their lives that there's just no opportunity in the day for keeping fit. However at the same time they usually sigh as they mention how they would like to be fitter and how good they feel after exercise.

Good health starts with getting fitter

If you want to maintain good health, then it involves some regular physical activity. I'm not necessarily suggesting long workouts, especially if time is not on your side, but instead simply doing something extra each day towards becoming more fit and toned. This could be walking to the local shops instead of taking the car, taking a brisk walk during your lunch break, or even increasing the pace when you walk so you can walk further in the same time. For some of us, this could even mean going to the gym!

What are the benefits for you of doing a little extra activity?

It is thought that regular activity, even just two 30 minute activity sessions per week, can noticeably increase our confidence and make us feel good. Not only this, exercise also helps us to achieve more and be more successful by:

- increasing our alertness and energy levels

- improving concentration and motivation

- encouraging a restful sleep, and

- creating opportunities – by meeting people and socialising.

What's important is that you find an activity that you enjoy.

What activity do you enjoy?

There are so many different activities to choose from, whether it's cycling with the family at the weekends, a swim in the local pool or workouts at the gym, there's bound to be something to your taste.

Some people see the time they spend doing activity as wasted. However, it is an important investment in your health. I often ask clients to remember how great they feel after they have exercised. I must admit I never regret going to the gym as I always feel so good after a workout – energised and more confident.

How to get the most from your activity session

To get the most from your chosen activity, use the time just for you to focus on yourself. Whether you listen to your favourite music, read books, listen to educational podcasts, or just enjoy being mindful of your body, you can make the time worthwhile. For instance whilst cycling on the exercise bike I use the time to read something related to what I'm working on at that time (or quite often to keep up with the latest fashions by reading a magazine!). And during my 20-minute walk to my therapy clinic, I use the time to run through the therapy sessions I have already pre-planned with my clients. While I'm doing this, I'm also being mindful of my body – feeling my muscles move, hearing my breathing; aware of my lungs filling with clean, energising air.

Your personal fitness commitment

I have prepared three easy steps towards fitness.

- *Step 1* involves reviewing your current lifestyle and activity levels so you can see where you may need to make changes.

- *Step 2* is about thinking about when you can fit activity into your lifestyle and what activity you enjoy.

- *Step 3* is about taking action and committing to your chosen activity. You can motivate yourself to do this by thinking about how good you will feel after.

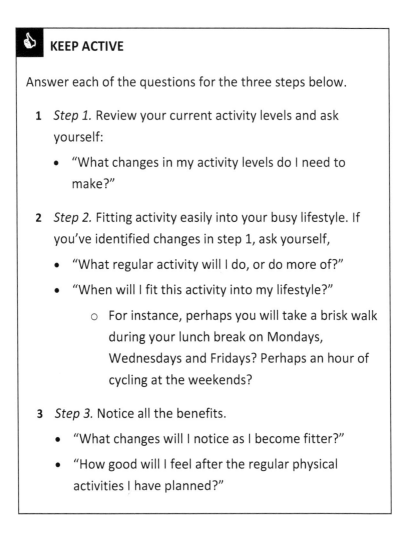

👆 **KEEP ACTIVE**

Answer each of the questions for the three steps below.

1 *Step 1.* Review your current activity levels and ask yourself:

- "What changes in my activity levels do I need to make?"

2 *Step 2.* Fitting activity easily into your busy lifestyle. If you've identified changes in step 1, ask yourself,

- "What regular activity will I do, or do more of?"
- "When will I fit this activity into my lifestyle?"
  - o For instance, perhaps you will take a brisk walk during your lunch break on Mondays, Wednesdays and Fridays? Perhaps an hour of cycling at the weekends?

3 *Step 3.* Notice all the benefits.

- "What changes will I notice as I become fitter?"
- "How good will I feel after the regular physical activities I have planned?"

Listen to your body

Remember to listen to your body and build up at a pace that's right for you, especially if you're not so used to exercise. Notice with regular activity how you become more toned, more confident and how your body feels fitter and healthier. You might even notice your clothes become slightly looser in the process.

Use the following activity to practice being mindful as you exercise.

☝ MINDFUL EXERCISE

Whatever activity you choose, enjoy how it makes you feel knowing you're on your way to a fitter, healthier body.

1 Having done the *Keep Active* exercise and chosen an activity, now make it happen.

2 As you exercise, you can use the time to become more in tune with your body by practising mindfulness (Chapter 1, Day 3).

   • For instance,

       o If you're swimming, feel the sensation of your body gliding comfortably through the water.

       o If you're walking, notice the movement of your muscles and the sensation of the surface beneath your feet with each step you take.

       o If you're cycling, become aware of sensation of a cool breeze against your face as you ride.

Day 2: Think your body healthy

Changing your mindset to programme your body towards health and fitness

Now that you're on your way to improving your fitness, if you want to maintain it in the long-term it is important to have the right mindset. For example, our local gym is usually crammed with new members early in January. The equipment is whirring away as people are eager and motivated to get fit to fulfil their annual New Year's Resolution. Then, usually by February, the gym is deserted as the initial novelty wears off and people revert back to their previous 'settings'.

How can I remain motivated to be fit and healthy?

If you want to maintain your new lifestyle beyond the initial enthusiasm you need it to become habit through repetition. Use the power of your mind to keep yourself motivated. Since whatever you tend to think about is more likely to happen, you can use quality thoughts as well as picturing what you want to achieve. Today I will show you how. Better still, you don't need to wait until the New Year to get started. You can motivate yourself now as every moment of every day is a chance to make a change.

Create a powerful positive body image

Repeatedly thinking about your body in a positive light helps your mind become clear about what you want. For instance, visualising your body as fit, toned and healthy will help you get into this mindset. Even by doing this you may notice how your behaviours automatically begin to change – perhaps having more motivation to exercise regularly or eat healthily.

I'm going to share with you an easy yet powerful visualisation technique that will powerfully change your mindset towards a positive, fit and healthy version of yourself. As you do this, use all your senses to really enjoy the experience. That way you will quickly begin to create a positive body image.

I would suggest finding a calm quiet place to do this activity. It may help to close your eyes so you can really focus on what you want.

👍 **THINK YOUR BODY FIT AND HEALTHY**

1 Use the *1-Minute Breathe in Calm* activity from Chapter 1, Day 1 (Breathe in through your nose for a count of 4, hold for 7, breathe out slowly for 8) to relax yourself.

2 Imagine you have achieved your health goal. For instance your goal might be to be fitter, slimmer and healthier or all of these things. Use all your senses to make the image as compelling and motivating as you can.

- See your body exactly the way you want it to look.
- Feel the sensation of your body comfortably exercised, toned, slim and feeling good.
- Notice how good positive emotions make you feel. Perhaps happy, motivated and smiling.
- Hear those compliments.
- Experience your positive thoughts at having achieved your goal.
- Imagine yourself taking regular activity and really enjoying how it makes you feel.

3 Let go of any old excuses or unhelpful thoughts.

- If you find old excuses or unhelpful thoughts creeping in, use the STOP-ERASE-REPLACE technique (*How to Think Positive*, Chapter 1, Day 4) to replace the thoughts with positive alternatives.

Practice makes permanent

Repeat the *Think Your Body Fit and Healthy* activity at least once every 2 or 3 days for the next few weeks. As you become more experienced, imagine yourself fit, toned, healthy or exactly how you want to be when you're out and about, at home or as often as you can. That way, you can be changing your body image for the better without even needing to set aside time in your busy day!

Remember also to keep going with the Chapter 1 activities so you not only remain calm but also optimise your health at the same time. For instance, if you're feeling stressed then use the *1-Minute Breathe in Calm* (Chapter 1, Day 1), or if you're having trouble sleeping then use the *Sleep Enhancing Techniques* (Chapter 1, Day 6).

Day 3: Past food associations

Whether your health goal is to reduce your weight or simply to maintain a healthy weight, you will benefit from today's activity. Today you will find out some of the reasons you eat in the way you do – something that is key to gaining control over your eating.

What food associations have you developed in the past?

We form many associations with food during our life. Most of these behaviours and triggers are formulated during our early years. An example that I hear commonly from my clients, is being brought up to eat everything on their plates. Because of this, they tell me that they find leaving any excess food wasteful, and instead will overeat.

Certainly I remember celebrating with food as a child. Birthday parties of cakes, biscuits and crisps were commonplace and I used to enjoy sweets as treats when I was younger. As an adult, I was initially unaware that I had formed other associations. For instance, automatically ordering a slice of cake whenever I went out for afternoon tea. Now whenever I go out I think to myself, "Am I really hungry?" and if I am, I can now choose a healthier option, such as a piece of fruit, instead.

Becoming aware of your past associations with food

The first step in gaining control over your eating and establishing a healthy relationship with food, is to understand how you eat now. Think back to times you've eaten in the past when you weren't truly hungry. What were the reasons? Was it because the clock said it was 'time to eat' or because you walked past the local shop and could smell sizzling bacon sandwiches?

Distinguishing physical from emotional hunger

Often we eat for reasons other than hunger. Emotions play a part in this so you may find yourself eating to mask a particular emotion you find uncomfortable. There are some differences and ways you can tell true physical hunger from emotional hunger. For instance if you find your hunger tends to come on very fast, you crave specific foods (especially those high in calories) and you have a desire to eat immediately, then it's likely you are experiencing emotional hunger.

If you think about the last time you ate when you weren't feeling hungry, does this sound familiar?

What am I feeling?

The next activity I've designed will help you recognise emotional hunger <u>and</u> do away with the need to eat at these times. You will be replacing emotional hunger with a new healthier response that you will choose. To help you I've created the *'Assessing Hunger Guide'*.

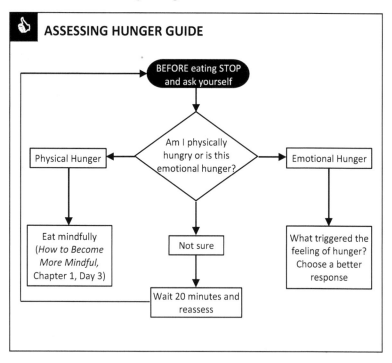

How to use the 'Assessing Hunger Guide'

This guide will help you to re-learn to listen to your natural hunger levels. It will also help you to quickly distinguish true physical hunger from emotional signals. In each case, eat before you feel completely ravenous otherwise there may be a tendency to overeat. Ensure that you make healthy food choices too.

<u>Before</u> you eat, decide whether you are physically or emotionally hungry. It is quite common for clients who frequently diet to be unaware of their hunger levels. Therefore I have included a 'not sure' category. If you're 'not sure', wait 20 minutes and find something else to do. Then start back at the top of the guide by asking yourself whether you're hungry. After reassessing, if you are still unsure then initially you may need to use outside signs. For instance, if it has been more than a few hours since you last ate, then you are more likely to be physically hungry.

Once you become more in tune with your hunger signals and notice that you are experiencing emotions rather than actual hunger, ask yourself what triggered the feeling of hunger? It may be a particular emotion, or simply a habit. Once you've identified the emotion or habit, then you choose your preferred response. For instance, if you notice you eat when you're bored, go for a brisk walk outdoors instead or do something you enjoy. An emotion that commonly seems to trigger emotional eating in my clients is loneliness. They often tell me they eat more when they are at home by themselves. At times like this a good tip, instead of eating, is to meet up with a friend – or at least telephone someone you enjoy talking to and have a good chat.

When you recognise true hunger, listen to your body. It will let you know how hungry you are and when it is time to eat. To begin with, take particular care when you're tired as the signals can be even more subtle.

👍 **ASSESSING HUNGER ACTIVITY**

Refer to the *Assessing Hunger Guide* each time you eat during the next week. Eat only when you recognise you are physically hungry and remember to eat mindfully.

Soon with regular practice you will automatically know when you are truly hungry and easily be able to eat only at these times.

Day 4: A fresh start

Whether your goal is to reduce weight, or simply to improve your overall wellbeing, good health starts with the right nutrition. It's not only the amount of food we eat that's important but also the type of foods. Eating a healthy balance of fresh natural foods signals to our body that we care about it and it will reward us with better health.

Motivation to make healthy food choices

The aim of today is to encourage you to enjoy making healthier food choices. The best way to do this initially is to get rid of temptations. So if you're in the habit of eating foods high in fat, sugar, salt or containing artificial ingredients, then put this book down for a moment whilst you rummage through the kitchen cupboards or desk drawers and throw out those old unhealthy snacks or processed ready meals.

Planning your new healthy start

I will show you how to develop a natural preference for healthy eating. I find the best way to do this is to plan my meals before I go shopping. To help you, I've created the meal planner (below) so you can plan nutritious meals and healthy snacks. As we are creatures of habit, quite often I find that my clients eat the same foods, so by planning meals, you can check that you're getting a good balance and variety. I usually plan out 2 or 3 days in advance, but plan out as many as you choose. After you've been planning for a few weeks, you'll have different plans that you can mix and match. Make sure the plan is realistic and motivates you.

If you're prone to emotional eating then keep your meal planner with you during the day so you can follow it and maintain your new healthy approach. Remember to take it with you to the supermarket too so you know what you need to buy. If you need any help with making healthy eating choices or how to get a good balance of all the food groups, have a look in your local library for some good books on the subject.

Day	Breakfast	Lunch	Evening Meal	Healthy Snacks

MENU PLANNER

Make your food planner as enticing and appealing as you can. Why not include new healthy recipes or trying a different fruit or vegetable each week. Enjoy the sensory experience and how healthy eating makes you feel good.

How can I become more motivated to eat healthily?

Now that you have your meals planned out we need to develop a preference for making healthy food choices. Even if you already do this, the technique I will show you will help you to understand the reasons you make the choices you do.

Your body is always listening and responding to what you are thinking. Each time you decide to eat, you experience a 'food thought'. You might be unaware of this but it influences the food choices you make.

Becoming mindful of your 'food thoughts'

Just as you discovered in Chapter 1, by becoming mindful of your thoughts, you can make them work better for you. Let's start with an example. Imagine you're eating out and you think, "I deserve a treat – I'll order chips with my meal tonight." In this case you are automatically giving yourself permission to go ahead. But if you were to be aware of this thought process, you could replace the 'food thought' with something better such as, "I deserve to look good and feel healthy – I'll choose a jacket potato instead of chips." This will help to inspire you towards your optimum body health goal. Of course, this is only an example. Choose thoughts that work best and inspire you. Ultimately the more you replace sabotaging thoughts with healthier options, the faster you will gain control over your eating.

The following activity is similar to the *How to Think Positive* from Chapter 1, Day 4. I've combined it with a visualisation too so you can practice both the *Stress Busting* (Chapter 1) and *Enhancing Body Health* (Chapter 2) techniques together to save you time.

☝ MOTIVATE YOURSELF TO MAKE HEALTHY FOOD CHOICES

1 Before you eat, take a moment to listen to your 'food thoughts'. Some examples might be:

- "One small piece of cake won't matter. I'll start again with my healthy eating tomorrow."

- "I've eaten unhealthily this morning. I may as well blow it for the rest of the day."

- "I deserve a treat."

2 Replace any thoughts that take you away from your body health goal with more inspiring alternatives such as:

- "Being slim, fit and healthy is more important to me than a few moments of enjoyment."

- "I can't change the past, but I can get my goal back on track by making healthy balanced choices for the rest of the day."

- "I deserve to be slim, fit and healthy. I can treat myself to a non-food reward, such as going for a pleasant relaxing walk with friends, or settling down to a good movie."

➡

Initially if you experience any inner resistance, remember that the more you avoid giving into it, the easier it will be to resist in the future. Alternatively, adopting a mindset of 'do it just for today', and then repeating this each day, helps some people to make changes one small step at a time.

3 Visualise yourself making fresh, natural and balanced food choices when:

- at the supermarket or local shop
- eating out (restaurants, cafés, at friends' houses, at work)
- eating at home
- or on holiday.

You may find that 'Post-It' notes strategically placed in your home (especially in the kitchen) and on your desk help to trigger these positive, supportive thoughts throughout your day.

Now armed with your appealing food planner, helpful thoughts and improved ability to assess hunger, you're making strides in taking control over your food choices and eating behaviours. Be proud.

Day 5: Listening to your body

In Day 4 I gave you a flavour of how you can become more motivated to make healthy food choices. Today we're going to build on the techniques of listening to our body as well as combining the techniques of mindfulness from Chapter 1. I will also be sharing with you a powerful tip that will allow you to enjoy your food more, naturally eat less and help you maintain a healthy body weight.

…and the secret?

Eating s-l-o-w-l-y and mindfully.

It might seem simple and obvious, but how many of us actually do this? My clients usually tell me that they often eat on the run – and tend to eat very quickly. By doing this, fast eaters can eat at least 200 extra calories each day than those who take time to enjoy their food.

Limit your portions

Another common thing I've noticed is that some people tend to pile up their plates with food. If you do this you are much more likely to overeat than if you gave yourself a smaller portion. Later in this chapter I will explain how to eat with control regardless of how much food is on your plate. In the meantime though, I recommend becoming more aware of how much you eat and limiting your portion sizes. You can always come back for more at a later time if you recognise you're still hungry.

How to open a packet of biscuits and only eat one

A worry that many people share is the ability to open a box or packet of food, and just have a small amount. If you find this difficult, imagine for a moment what it would be like if you were able to open a pack of biscuits, have one, and enjoy it without feeling tempted to finish the pack. Well the good news is that you *can* do this. The exceptional techniques I will show you later in this chapter will give you this control. In the meantime dividing any large packs of foods into smaller portions can be helpful. Always avoid eating out of a packet or a box. Instead put the food in a bowl or on a plate so you can register how much you've eaten.

Make mealtimes an enjoyable relaxing experience

To become more mindful of your eating and better able to listen to what your body needs, it can be helpful to dine in relaxing surroundings. If you want to avoid overeating then I recommend sitting at a table rather than in front of the TV. Having some quiet time to enjoy the different textures and tastes of foods and being more 'in tune' with your body will help you to recognise that feeling of fullness sooner. That way you are likely to eat only what you need.

How to eat with control

I've prepared a guide for you that combines the techniques you have been practising this week, with mindfulness. Whilst the guide is simple, the suggestions have proven to be very powerful in gaining control with eating. I suggest keeping a copy of this guide with you initially so you can refer to it each time you eat.

YOUR POWERFUL GUIDE TO EATING WITH CONTROL

1 Eat only when physically hungry. (See *Assessing Hunger* activity, Chapter 2, Day 3).

2 *Choose fresh natural foods.* Follow your *Menu Planner* (Chapter 2, Day 4).

3 Limit your portion sizes.

4 *Sit down to eat.* Avoid eating on the run or fridge-grazing. Sit down, relax and enjoy your food. Avoid eating in front of the TV.

5 *Be mindful.* Stop what you're doing. Switch off the TV and instead focus on being mindful of what you're eating.

- Take small bites.

- Thoroughly chew your food and really enjoy savouring each mouthful. Notice the different textures and tastes.

- *Eat s-l-o-w-l-y*.

- Put your knife, fork, or spoon down between mouthfuls.

- Avoid talking whilst chewing. Swallow your food before talking.

- Sip water from time-to-time between mouthfuls. It will slow down your eating and help you recognise fullness earlier.

By following these techniques, overeating will quickly become a thing of the past. Remember to combine this healthy way of eating with your regular physical activity (See *Mindful Exercise* from Chapter 2, Day 1) and *Think Your Body Fit and Healthy* (See Chapter 2, Day 2). If you put these tips into practice you will be well on your way to being naturally slim, fit and healthy long-term.

Day 6: Reset the full signal

Do you ever find yourself eating even though you know you've had enough to eat? Perhaps you feel like the full switch is no longer there?

When do you stop eating?

Many of us only stop eating after we feel 'bloated' and overfull. When do you usually stop eating? Is it when you recognise you've had enough to eat? When you've eaten all the food on your plate? Or when you've finished the entire pack of whatever you're eating? Now instead of feeling bloated, imagine how much nicer it would be to enjoy feeling comfortably satisfied after a meal.

Have you been brought up to eat everything on your plate?

I've also observed that many of us are brought up to eat everything on our plates. To overcome this hurdle involves recognising that it's better to leave any excess food than it is to overeat and feel uncomfortable – after all, second and third helpings never taste the same as the first!

To retrain your mind to feel relaxed about throwing away excess food, I would recommend that you leave a little food on your plate after each meal over the next few days. This might only be a single mouthful but will be a powerful message to your mind to become comfortable with this. Later in this chapter I will show you how to recognise naturally when you've had enough to eat – and you may be surprised to find that you may need less food than you think.

If you're still struggling with the idea of throwing away good food, then some foods can be covered over and put in the fridge for another time. Sometimes I even divide my meals into healthy snacks. For instance, if lunch is a sandwich and yoghurt, if I recognise I've had enough to eat after my sandwich, I will save the yoghurt as a snack for the afternoon should I feel physically hungry later.

Listen for the subtle signals of hunger and fullness

I admit that if you're used to eating more than you need, the signals of hunger and fullness can be quite subtle. Let me reassure you that they become more obvious with practice. In fact, I was amazed at how quickly my mind relearnt how to hear the vague signals. Eating s-l-o-w-l-y and mindfully was key in helping me to achieve this.

Now I tend to eat small amounts regularly depending on what my body needs and when I register the true sensations of hunger. This keeps me from feeling ravenous – so I'm less likely to overeat, and also maintains my blood sugar levels to keep my mood positive.

'Slow' foods can help you to eat less

It can take at least 30 minutes for our brain to register we've eaten and are sufficiently full. I've noticed that for me, it can often take anything up to an hour. Choosing 'slow' foods that require more chewing, such as apples, crunchy vegetable crudités, wholegrain crackers or crunchy salad helps me to feel fuller sooner. It's a good tip I share with my clients and gets them eating more healthily too!

The next activity I will share with you will ensure you only eat what you physically need. It's simple, powerful and takes no extra time out of your day.

👍 RESET YOUR FULL SIGNAL

1 Use *Your Powerful Guide to Eating with Control* (Chapter 2, Day 5) to eat slowly and mindfully.

2 Pause regularly throughout your meal. Ask yourself, "Have I had enough to eat now?"

3 If you're not sure, stop eating. Take a moment to reassess if you've had enough to eat.

4 If you recognise early stirrings of fullness, stop eating. Allow a thought to enter your mind, "I've had enough to eat now." This is your full signal. By doing this you are powerfully changing your mindset to automatically respond to fullness by stopping eating.

5 Throw away the excess food. Remove your plate from the table and immediately discard any excess food to avoid tempting yourself to nibble at the leftovers! If I'm dining out, I find it helpful to cover any excess food with my serviette.

6 If you're out with friends, thank them for a wonderful meal and know that any food left is excess food and is not required. If well-meaning friends or family try to tempt you with seconds, be strong. Remember it's so much nicer to feel comfortably satisfied than bloated and overfull.

> **7** Hold off dessert for at least 30 minutes. If you do this, you'll probably find that you don't need dessert after all!

Summary guide to eating with control

Since we eat several times per day there are many opportunities to practice eating with control. To help you I've prepared a summary of the powerful techniques. I find it helpful to keep a copy with me to refer to each time I eat.

- I eat only when I am physically hungry.
- I choose fresh natural foods.
- I sit down to eat.
- I eat s-l-o-w-l-y, and chew my food thoroughly.
- I stop eating when I register the 'full signal'.

Day 7: Hydration for health

Do you drink enough water during the day? If you're not getting enough fresh water then you're not alone. Nearly every client I see tells me that they need to drink more water. Yet many of us are so used to reaching for a coffee, we often forget to do this.

The benefits of drinking fresh thirst quenching water

Drinking 1 or 2 litres of water each day (depending on activity levels) is essential for good health. If you want to feel more alert and energised, have good looking skin, and even avoid feelings of mild depression, then I recommend getting into the habit of drinking water. If you're not a fan of the taste of water, then non-caffeinated herbal teas or warm water with a squeeze of lemon juice are good too.

What are you drinking?

When I was writing this book I started recording all the different drinks I consumed each day and the amounts. I was quite surprised by what I found. I've included this activity to help you to discover how much, and the types of drink, you typically have each day.

When you fill out this questionnaire, think about the drinks you had yesterday then fill in the boxes with your answers.

WHAT ARE YOU DRINKING?		
Water	☐	glasses (or ml) per day
Coffee	☐	cups per day
Tea	☐	cups per day
Herbal tea	☐	cups per day
Fresh juices	☐	glasses per day
Fruit smoothies	☐	glasses per day
Fruit squash	☐	glasses per day
Carbonated drinks	☐	cans/bottles per day
Alcohol	☐	glasses per day
Other	☐	(specify)

What did you find?

If you look over your intake for the drinks you had yesterday, what did you find? Are there any changes you need to make? For instance, do you need to swap a couple of cups of coffee per day for water or herbal tea? Remember caffeine stays in the body for between 6 and 8 hours so avoid drinking it after 3pm if you want to get a good sleep. Caffeine may also have a similar effect on the body as chronic stress. Whilst I appreciate it's about getting a balance, making just a few small changes to reduce your caffeine intake can make a big difference to your health and wellbeing.

I would also recommend limiting your intake of alcohol if you want to get a better quality sleep and reduce stress. Alcohol stimulates the appetite too and contains a lot of empty calories – so it's best avoided if you want to reduce your weight.

If you found it difficult to remember what you had to drink yesterday, then simply complete this questionnaire throughout today then assess your responses at the end of the day. If you found this activity helpful, you might also like to use a similar process to record what you ate during the day. It can lead to some very interesting findings indeed! It is quite surprising to see all those little nibbles that you have throughout the day that you hadn't previously counted!

Remember to drink water

I now keep a 1 litre bottle of refreshing water at my desk and set myself reminders to sip water throughout the day. Water is a natural appetite suppressant so I often sip it 20–25 minutes before meals to prevent me confusing hunger with dehydration. I can comfortably swap a traditional caffeine-containing breakfast tea for some caffeine-free herbal tea varieties.

I do confess that I enjoy the occasional carbonated drink, even though I'm aware they're usually loaded with preservatives, phosphates, artificial sweeteners or refined sugars. Using the techniques of mindfulness in this chapter, helped me to appreciate drinking water more and now I only occasionally indulge in fizzy drinks.

Start your day with gentle refreshing warm lemon water

If you want a gentle start to your morning a squeeze of fresh lemon in warm water is the way to go. I will often drink warm lemon water just before bed too as it's a good way to calm down and relax.

Using mindfulness to keep hydrated

Throughout the last two chapters you've used many different techniques – including mindfulness – to alter your mindset towards being healthy and more relaxed. You can also use this technique to become more mindful of sipping water throughout the day. To do this, review your answers to the *What Are You Drinking?* activity and then follow the tips below.

👍 HOW TO HYDRATE

1 Replace at least one drink containing caffeine, alcohol or carbonated drinks with fresh water, herbal tea or warm lemon water. If you don't drink caffeine, alcohol or fizzy drinks then be proud that you're investing in your health.

2 Keep a bottle of water with you and sip throughout the day. Set yourself reminders if necessary to jog your memory.

3 As you sip water during the day, use the time to take a moment to relax and practice your *Think Your Body Fit and Healthy* (Chapter 2, Day 2).

Keeping comfortably hydrated will help you towards your overall body health goal. Remember as you practice your

Keep Active activity (Chapter 2, Day 1) today to adjust the amount you drink accordingly.

CHAPTER 2 SUMMARY

This week I have given you a flavour of what good health is all about. Feeling good comes from listening and responding to the signals of both your mind and your body. Becoming 'in tune' with ourselves takes minimal time and yet is so effective for long-term health. It also puts us back in control.

I now encourage you to continue to eat a healthy balanced diet, get plenty of rest combined with regular physical activity throughout this programme. Practising the Stress Busting techniques alongside will also complement your overall health and wellbeing. To help you to optimise your health in the long-term, I've added a summary which is the essence of this chapter. All you need to do is follow the techniques that work best for you. By making one small change each day, you'll quickly see a dramatic improvement in your overall health and wellbeing.

- *Know what you need to change.* Decide what aspects of your health need to be improved and how you can achieve this. Then take action each day towards this goal. It doesn't have to take much time and has big rewards.

- *Create a healthy mindset.* Being fit and healthy starts with the right mindset. Use mindfulness and visualisation to create the perfect body image that drives you towards good health.

- *Keep active.* Doing something active each day. Find something you enjoy and vary the activity to keep you motivated. Make an active lifestyle habit. Get rid of any old excuses using the STOP-ERASE-REPLACE technique (*How to Think Positive*, Chapter 1, Day 4).

- *Remember to sip water.* Keep a bottle of fresh, cooling water with you to sip throughout the day. Warm lemon water is a good drink to start the day. Replace caffeinated drinks with herbal teas and water. Even just replacing one caffeinated drink with a healthier alternative can make a difference.

Eat with control

- *Eat only when you are physically hungry.* Be aware of any old food associations, triggers and emotions so that you eat only when you are naturally hungry. Hunger signals are subtle. Being mindful of them will quickly help you to know when you actually need to eat. Avoid becoming ravenous as there is a tendency to overeat.

- *Be mindful of 'food thoughts'.* Focus on what you want to achieve and how good you will feel. Make your thoughts work for you.
- *Find new ways of dealing with emotions.* Recognise emotions and choose better ways to deal with them rather than eating.

- *Choose fresh natural foods.* Replace foods high in fat, sugar, salt and artificial ingredients with fresh natural foods. Plan natural healthy meals.

- *Sit down to eat.* Make mealtimes a relaxing and enjoyable experience. Switch off the TV and use the time to relax and savour your food.

- *Eat s-l-o-w-l-y.* The golden rule for eating with control. Take small bites, chew, savour, enjoy.

- *Stop eating as soon as you recognise you're full.* Ask yourself regularly when eating *"Have I had enough to eat now?"* Stop eating as soon as you hear the full signal (the thought *"I've had enough to eat now!"*).

REVIEW YOUR PROGRESS 1

How are you getting on?

At this stage it is worth considering how far you've come over the past couple of weeks. Notice what works well for you and any areas that may need a little extra attention.

Be proud of your accomplishments

The four key questions below will help you to note down how you're doing. Feel pleased with your achievements, however small, and take action on any items that you still need to work on. Think about the changes you made in reducing stress, as well as the improvements to your overall body health when you complete this section.

Your four key progress questions

1. What changes have you noticed?

    _____

    _____

    _____

2. What techniques worked well for you so far?

    _____

    _____

    _____

3. What areas need further work?

_____

_____

_____

4. What action will you take to make these changes?

_____

_____

_____

CHAPTER THREE

*

Projecting
Confidence

What is confidence?

Over the years I have had the privilege of working with many talented clients who wanted to become more confident. Some, were keen to project confidence in business or social settings. For others, it was more important to develop an inner belief in themselves and their abilities. In either case, true confidence comes from feeling good about yourself. *And if you don't already?* Then the good news is that confidence can be learnt and I will show you how.

Believe in yourself

As we embark on this week, I will show you some really easy and exceptional ways that will get you not only looking, but also feeling really confident. Before I share these with you though, I want you to ask yourself this question.

"What does confidence mean to me?"

To help you answer this question, imagine you woke up this morning to find that you were truly confident. A powerful inner belief in yourself and your abilities. What would this be like?

Being confident means different things to different people. I have received many different responses to this question over the years. However, most clients tell me it's about feeling good in themselves and being able to do anything they choose without fear. And if you were to imagine you were this confident now, how do you look, feel and sound? How do you project confidence in your:

- Appearance
  - How do you look?
  - How do you present yourself?
  - What is your style?

- Posture
  - How do you stand?
  - How do you sit?
  - How do you walk and move to show you are powerfully confident?

- Voice
  - How do you project your voice?
  - What is the tone of your voice?
  - What words do you use?

Think yourself confident

It really is possible to wake up each day and feel good about yourself.

And the secret. ...?

Being confident begins with having that all important mindset. The thoughts you have about yourself shape who you are and how you feel. And if you want to start feeling good, it needs to begin with thinking good things.

Take a moment to consider what thoughts you would have about yourself if you were powerfully confident. What could you achieve with this positive mindset? How good would it feel to be this confident?

Make confidence your new habit

There are several different aspects to being confident which we will cover this week. Not only will I explain how to boost your self-esteem but I will also illustrate how to develop an assertive confidence. By making confidence your new habit, by the end of the week you will not only be feeling and speaking more confidently, but walking taller too!

Day 1: Confident in the *Current You*

Why does it always seem so much easier to focus on our faults and bad habits rather than on the good things? And yet really this type of thinking doesn't get us to where we want to be – and it certainly doesn't help us to feel good about ourselves!

Becoming more confident starts with getting rid of unwanted thoughts such as "What's the point, I'll never succeed" or "I'm not good at anything". I guarantee there will be things that you are good at! So why do we think in this way? Some clients tell me it's so that if things don't work out the way they wanted they won't be disappointed. But is this really a good way to think?

Thoughts not facts

Having recognised that thoughts can be distorted and are not necessarily fact, we can begin to question them and make them serve us better. But how do you change how you think about yourself when those thoughts just 'pop into your head'?

The answer …

... by reminding yourself of all your positive qualities and the things you're good at. I appreciate this isn't always easy to do, especially when you are not accustomed to thinking in this way. When do you last remember thinking something good about you? Or being proud of your achievements?

Remember all the good things about you

Since confidence starts with reminding ourselves of our positive qualities – and yes we do all have them – I'm going to take you step-by-step through a technique that gets you recognising the positive real you. I would recommend starting with a few deep breaths using your *1-Minute Breathe in Calm* technique (breathe in through your nose for a count of 4, hold for 7, breathe out for 8) and then you're ready to begin.

👍 **RECOGNISING THE POSITIVE YOU**

1 Reflect back on a proud moment of your life. Experience those good feelings as you relive your success. Listen to the compliments you receive and recall all the wonderful things people say about you.

2 Think about the things you do well and all of your positive qualities. Appreciate the extent of your strengths, skills and achievements.

Note: It is important to get yourself feeling really good for this technique to work well. If you're not quite feeling it, then it may help you to imagine seeing yourself through the eyes of someone who really cares about you.

3 As those good feelings start to flow, double it, triple it, make it ten times more powerful so you can feel a powerful inner belief and confidence flow through every part of you.

4 Keep this good confident feeling with you throughout your day. If the good feeling should start to fade, repeat this activity.

Start your day right

When I first started doing this, on waking each morning, I would practice my breathing and then spend a few minutes recalling all the good things about me. Over time I found that this positive self-belief became habit and has done wonders for my outward confidence too. For the rest of this week, get your day off to a great start with this activity. Remember to *Keep Active* as regular exercise will boost your confidence and fast track you towards a developing powerful self-esteem.

Day 2: Confident in the *New You*

Previously ...

Yesterday we looked at all the good things about you as you are now. The purpose of doing this was to identify your unique and special qualities and get you feeling good about yourself.

But what if there are things you still want to change and where do you start?

Before you can make changes to your confidence, you need to identify what qualities and behaviours you would like to have. To do this, I find it easiest to think about someone I admire who is very confident. This can be someone you know, such as a good friend or colleague, or it might even be a TV personality or celebrity.

Take a moment to do this now. As you do this, what behaviours and good qualities spring to mind?

What you're likely to find is that you already have many of these qualities and simply need to refine them a little more. That way you can become the ideal person you aspire to be.

Transforming from the 'Current You' into the 'Ideal You'

Identifying the 'Ideal You' is an important first step to becoming more self-assured and confident. It helps you to discover what you need to change. Armed with this knowledge, you can then start the transformation process from the 'Current You' into the 'Ideal You'.

Today's activity will talk you step-by-step through this. To get the most out of it I would recommend beginning with the *Recognising the Positive You* activity from yesterday. This will get you feeling good about yourself and into the right frame of mind to begin the transformation.

👍 WHO IS THE IDEAL YOU?

1 Imagine you are exactly how you want to be – the 'Ideal You'. Picture yourself going through your day in this new confident way. Notice how you:

- Look. What is your style and appearance? How do you carry yourself?

- Feel.

- Act or respond to situations.

- Think. What positive thoughts do you have about yourself?

2 Recognise what you need to change now to become this ideal you.

3 Take action. What steps do you need to make to become this ideal version of yourself? Set yourself a realistic and achievable target towards this new you. Even changing one thing each day can make a tremendous difference. Start now!

4 After you've taken action, look back over your day. Did you make this change? If not, what do you need to do differently to achieve your target?

5 Set self another target for tomorrow.

Act the person you aspire to be

Recognising what you aspire to be like and taking action does require commitment. However, the more you imagine the person you desire to be, the more you will become that person and enjoy being confident every day.

Day 3: Perfect posture

I find that I can tell those people who feel good simply by the way they carry themselves. They walk tall, their posture is upright and they appear relaxed. You can tell a lot about what someone thinks about themselves, and their mood, by the way they walk. Look around today and see if you notice this and think about what you observed. You'll most likely find that an energised and confident look is much more appealing (and approachable) than a slumped lethargic posture.

How is your posture?

Having a good posture has a really powerful effect on both the mind and the body. The first thing I see in clients suffering from depression is a tired, slumped posture. Simply by standing tall and walking with purpose we quickly begin to feel uplifted. And when we feel good in ourselves we naturally approach things in a more positive way and feel confident.

How do you currently stand, walk and move? Is your posture always upright yet relaxed as you walk with purpose? Or do you have a wilting posture and tired movements? When you think about this, how would you like your posture to be?

The effect of the mind on the body

We can all make a positive impression through perfect posture. As you practice the positive thinking activities in Chapter 1, you are likely to find that your posture naturally begins to become more relaxed, upright and positive. This is because the mind has a powerful effect on how we feel. Similarly if our posture is good, we're likely to think in a better way. With that in mind, I'm going to guide you through a technique to get you standing tall and walking with confidence.

👆 STANDING TALL AND WALKING WITH CONFIDENCE

1 Picture and feel a strong line attached to the top of your head, gently pulling you straight and tall towards the ceiling.

2 Look straight ahead.

3 Place your feet shoulder width apart, with your weight mostly on the balls of your feet.

4 Let your hands drop naturally to your sides.

5 Congratulations. Smile! You are now standing tall.

6 When you walk continue to feel that strong line, as you walk tall, with confidence and at a good pace.

7 Continue to stand and walk tall throughout the day by leaving yourself reminders.

How does having a good posture make you feel?

At the end of the day after practising walking tall and with confidence, did you notice any difference in how you felt? Did you feel more energised and good in yourself? Keep this perfect posture for the rest of the week until it becomes habit. That way you can enjoy not only feeling confident but also projecting confidence to the outside world.

Day 4: Find your own voice

As a hypnotherapist and trainer, I am aware that my voice is a powerful tool essential to my success. It is important that I not only project my voice well, but I am mindful of the tone I use and things that I say.

Now that you are on your way to becoming more confident you will need an equally assertive voice to match. Whilst there are several aspects to speaking with confidence, I've discovered that being perceived as confident is more about <u>how</u> you say things than the words you use. If you tend to use a lot of *"ums"*, *"ahs"*, *"well ..."* or apologetic speech such as *"I'm sorry ... (but I disagree with you),"* then you need to make some changes if you want to sound confident.

Other aspects of weak language which I notice a lot in people who are less confident are sentences which end with *"don't you think?"* This gives the impression that the person is not confident in what they are saying or looking for reassurance. And what about if you start sentences with *"I think I like that"* or *"I know I'm not describing this well..."*? Does this project confidence?

Sounding confident

Take a moment to reflect on how you currently speak. Do you tend to use weak language or powerful language? How do you project your voice? How fast do you speak? What is your tone?

Quite often making slight adjustments to your voice can improve how you are perceived. For today's activity I will share with you secrets of how to speak with confidence. Review each of the *Speaking with Confidence* suggestions that follow, then think about how your voice sounds now. What changes do you need to make to project confidence when you speak? Once you've identified this, practice making slight changes until your voice is exactly how you want it – powerful and confident.

👍 SPEAKING WITH CONFIDENCE

1 *To sound smart* when you speak, use a moderate pace.

- If you talk slowly, you may seem less intelligent, tired or bored.

- If you speak very fast, you may seem nervous. Slow it down slightly by pausing and taking the occasional deep breath.

2 *To avoid misunderstandings* speak with a clear, positive and firm tone to convey confidence and avoid misunderstandings.

- Avoid monotone as it conveys lack of assertiveness and people will quickly lose interest.

3 *Be heard.* Project your voice with appropriate volume for the situation.

- The volume of your voice reflects your emotional state – too loud may seem aggressive or angry; too soft conveys lack of authority.

- You can change the volume of your voice for impact too. For instance lowering your voice can cause the listener to concentrate more intently on what you are saying. Raising your voice momentarily can also add impact. However, avoid doing this too often. ➲

4 *To convey authority* deepen your voice slightly to convey power and authority.

- Deepening your voice (lowering the pitch) on certain words can affect the overall meaning as well as conveying confidence and authority whereas raising the pitch conveys doubt and uncertainty.

- To sound more assertive keep the tone even or lower it slightly at the end of a sentence.

5 *To be understood* speak clearly and pronounce words correctly.

- Practice using clear, crisp words and pronounce them properly to convey intelligence, confidence and competence.

- Avoid mumbling as it appears nervous, uneducated and lazy.

- If you're not sure how to pronounce a word (or what it means) then avoid using it.

6 *Think before speaking.* Choose your words carefully.

- Assertive people take a moment to think before they speak.

- Stop, pause, organise your thoughts then convey your message in a clear, concise statement. Speaking only for as long as needed creates mystery and makes the listener intrigued to find out more.

Throughout the next few days, think about how you currently speak and make any necessary changes to your voice to project your increasing confidence. When you speak clearly and with authority you will notice that people sit up and listen with interest. Enjoy trying out these different techniques until you find what works best for you.

Day 5: How to think yourself assertive

Now you have started to develop your confident mindset, posture and voice, I want to concentrate today on confident behaviours. As with any changes you want to make, it starts with developing the right mindset. So today I will show you an exceptionally easy yet powerful technique to change your thoughts towards assertiveness.

Believe you are already assertive

Simply by believing you are already assertive you will instantly become much more self-confident. Throughout the day let yourself be the confident, assertive person you aspire to be. When you do this, you will most likely find that your self-esteem is automatically lifted. Also, it helps to keep in mind that you are equally important as other people. By doing this you will find that you naturally start to become more aware of what you need and are able to clearly express what you want in an assertive and respectful way.

Being assertive has really helped me to confidently get through some of the most challenging situations with ease. I regularly use the following technique when I need to boost my assertiveness. It reminds me that I am just as important as others, and should be treated with respect.

> **👍 THINK YOURSELF ASSERTIVE**
>
> - Believe you are already assertive.
> - Throughout the day say silently to yourself, *"I am important."*

I noticed an instant and enormous difference in how I felt using this technique. You can even change the statement *"I am important"* to something that suits you best. For instance you might choose *"I am assertive"* or *"I am powerfully confident"*. Use this mind changing technique in combination with the *Standing Tall and Walking with Confidence* (Chapter 3, Day 3) and *Speaking with Confidence* (Chapter 3, Day 4) activities from earlier in this chapter for added impact. Remember to *Keep Active* (Chapter 2, Day 1) and get regular exercise as this is a great confidence booster too!

Day 6: How to behave assertively

I used to think that to be assertive I would have to be more extrovert. However, even the most reserved amongst us can be assertive by developing a positive self-image combined with a few confident behaviours and traits. In fact, once you have developed an assertive mindset it is likely that your behaviours will automatically become more confident. For instance, you may find that you feel more relaxed which will be reflected in your open posture and friendly expression.

What does it feel like to behave assertively?

To get you thinking in an assertive way remember a time when you felt very confident. What do you notice? How does it feel to be this confident? Reflect on how you deal with situations or how you would deal with things better if you were as confident as this every day.

Why become more assertive?

I've observed that when my clients are not able to express what they want appropriately, this can affect how they feel. So today we will look more closely at the confident behaviours of assertive people. I will also share with you some tips that have worked particularly well for my clients. It is possible to learn to be more self-assured and with a little practice, being assertive will quickly become an automatic habit for you.

Assertiveness tips and techniques

- *Use "I" Statements.* Assertive people take ownership by using *"I"* statements such as "I want ..." or "I feel ..." instead of "you" or "we". Strong *"I"* statements have three components:
  1. I feel (emotion) ...
  2. When you do (behaviour) ...
  3. The effects are (results or consequence to you) ...

  For example "I feel frustrated when you turn up late for meetings. I don't like having to repeat a discussion ..."

- *Make yourself visible.* Height and size gain attention. An upright and open posture looks assertive. When sitting, a good tip is to keep your head upright and shoulders square and to fill the natural space of your chair (without appearing intimidating). Keep your posture upright, open and relaxed.

- *Saying "no" assertively.* If you find it difficult to say "no" to avoid offending others, you can end up taking on too much leaving you too exhausted to do the things you enjoy. Each time you avoid saying "no" to things you don't want to do, you are automatically saying "no" to yourself and the people that matter to you by giving your time away to other things or people. To avoid devaluing yourself, change your focus from making others happy, and worrying about what they think, to being responsible for yourself. By doing this you will be perceived as truly assertive and respected more for it. The secret is to:

  o Just say "no" using a warm, pleasant yet powerful tone of voice.
  o Avoid apologising or justifying your reasons. You have a right to say "no".
  o Remember you are just as important as others.
  o And even if someone is persistent, be strong.

- *Speak with fact not emotion.* If you notice yourself becoming frustrated, despondent, or have difficulty explaining yourself clearly, then take a deep breath, think through what you want to say.

- *Use appropriate eye contact.* Assertive people use an appropriate amount of eye contact. If you find this uncomfortable then an easy technique is to look at the bridge of the nose of the person you are communicating with. It can give a perception of authority when you do this too!

Identify the behaviours above that you need to change or work on. Change one thing at a time and take it step-by-step. Use the following activity to practice these different aspects of assertive behaviour until they become comfortable and automatic for you.

👍 **INSTANT ASSERTIVENESS**

1 *Programme confidence.* Think back to situations where you would have benefitted from being more assertive.

- How did you respond?
- What was the reason?
- How will you respond differently now?

2 *Rehearse.* Practice these assertive behaviours with a good friend or family member until they become automatic.

3 *Take action.* Identify one small area where you would like to assert yourself better. For the rest of the day practice your new assertive behaviours and notice how people begin to respond differently. Remember to:

- Use "I" statements
- Have open and upright posture
- Speak with facts whilst maintaining eye contact
- Say "no" assertively.

Note: If you find this activity challenging then learn from someone who is already assertive. How do they act, look, sound? Notice their posture, the words they use and the way they confidently carry themselves.

Assertiveness is ultimately about being honest and open about what you're thinking and feeling and communicating it in a clear, respectful way. Being assertive is so powerful and will make a tremendous difference to how you feel and how you are perceived. However, be patient as it can take some time for the people around you to adapt to the new assertive you.

Day 7: Perfecting your appearance

I usually find that when I look my best, it makes me feel instantly more confident. Spending a little time each day on looking good also encourages me to adopt healthier behaviours.

The icing on the cake

When we look good, we feel good, and this is reflected in the way we present ourselves. The icing on the cake for your new-found confidence is to have the perfect 'look' and 'style' to match. With this mind, this is a good time to 'treat yourself'. I'm not talking about an excuse to indulge in cream cakes, but doing something really nice for yourself towards your appearance that gets you feeling really good. If your budget is limited, this doesn't even have to cost you anything. Simply do one thing nice for yourself today that makes you look and feel good.

For those who want to 'splash out' then enjoy investing a little time to spoil yourself today. Make sure you keep up your new look so you can enjoy feeling good about yourself and looking amazing every day.

> ☝ **PERFECT APPEARANCE**
>
> 1 Take any aspect of your appearance and set aside a little time to look your best. Whether it's a visit to the hair stylist for a new look; wearing your favourite outfit; or simply choosing to smile throughout the day, the aim is to look and feel good.
>
> 2 Remember to *Think Yourself Assertive* (Chapter 3, Day 5).
>
> 3 Use the *Instant Assertiveness* techniques (Chapter 3, Day 6).

Welcome, to the new you!

With regular practice of these confidence techniques you will be well on your way to radiating a positive self-esteem and powerful inner confidence. As you build on these skills you will naturally become more self-assured and the person you deserve and aspire to be. So keep those shoulders back and hold your head high as you project to the world the new confident you!

CHAPTER 3 SUMMARY

In this chapter I shared with you some exceptional techniques to develop a powerful inner belief to optimise your confidence. Anyone can be confident. You simply have to choose to be that way. The secret to changing you mindset for confidence is to believe that you already are confident and assertive. That way, as the people around you start to notice and compliment you, you can enjoy accepting the praise graciously and feeling even more self-assured.

The three key aspects to confidence are:

- having the right mindset

- acting confident (the right behaviours), and

- appearing confident (looking good).

And if you master all these, you have the complete package for optimum confidence.

Summary of techniques for a confident mindset

- *Believe in yourself.* Inner confidence starts with the right mindset and recognising all the good things about you. Be proud.

- *Act the person you aspire to be.* Anyone can be confident by believing they already are the person they want to be. By doing this you will become instantly more self-assured. If you find this challenging, use role models and follow their confident lead.

- *Make confidence your new habit.* When you wake up each morning start the day by choosing how you want to feel and you will respond accordingly.

Summary of techniques for confident behaviours

- *Be assertive.* Adopt the mindset that you are equally as important as others. Get comfortable at being assertive and saying *"no"* when you choose to. That way people will perceive you as more confident and treat you with respect.

- *Speak with a friendly yet assertive tone.* Make yourself heard by projecting your voice appropriately. Take time to think before speaking so you choose your words thoughtfully. Be clear in your communication and use a slightly deeper tone if you want to convey authority.

- *Keep active.* Regular exercise is a good behaviour to get into if you want an instant confidence boost.

Staying active will keep you both looking and feeling good about yourself.

Summary of techniques for looking confident

- *Stand tall.* Your posture reflects how you feel about yourself. To instantly look energised and confident, stand tall and walk with purpose.

- *Look your best.* Your appearance should complement your new confidence. Making the best of yourself will improve your self-esteem.

- *Smile.* Complete your confident look with a warm and friendly smile. It's an instant confidence boost and will make you even more appealing.

CHAPTER FOUR

*

Achieving Social Success

Achieving social success

Throughout the first three chapters you have been mastering your own thoughts and mind, and you will already be much more in tune with your body and emotions. You should notice that your confidence is beginning to increase too and as it does, you will be ready for the final tools to complete your toolkit, which are …

…*the secrets to achieving social success.*

Relationships are valuable

Developing successful and lasting relationships with others is one of the most valuable investments you will make. Relationships whether personal or professional require commitment and effort, but the rewards are well worth it.

Enjoy interacting with others

Remember these words as you read through this chapter. Approaching your interactions with others as something to enjoy will quickly have you climbing the ladder to social glory. As we go through this chapter I will demonstrate other tried and tested techniques that will enable you to create an immediate rapport with anyone you choose – whether friends, family or even your boss! By the end of this chapter, you will know secrets that get others instantly scrambling to spend time with you!

I have the answer

Whether your goal is to become a people magnet and instantly attract people to you, or whether you simply want to know the secrets of lasting and successful relationships, this chapter has something powerful to offer. But first, let's identify what social success is to you.

What are the essential ingredients for social success?

If you were to ask yourself this question, what would your answer be? What changes would you need to make in order to improve your current relationships or develop new ones? What things do you admire in other people? And what would make you an even better person to be around?

I will take you step-by-step through some insightful ways you can get answers to each of these questions. That way, you will find out not only how to appear instantly more intriguing, but also how you can be an even more special person to be around.

The only person you can change is yourself

Let's start this chapter with that all important mindset before we move onto looking at behaviours needed for social success. Keep in mind throughout that you cannot change other people. They are who they are. Instead put your energy and attention into being the best you can. That way you can still influence others by being an inspiring role model and you'll get to play a positive part in their development.

Day 1: Think yourself socially successful

I always look forward to every meeting with each of my clients. I find people fascinating and love the diversity and different views of the world that each holds. I approach each interaction as something to be enjoyed – just as I do when I spend time with really good friends. This helps others to feel important and appreciated by me.

How do you guarantee more successful interactions with others?

If you were to ask yourself this question:

"What approach and mindset would I need in order to get on better with others?"

What would your answer be? For me, I like to start by thinking that I am already socially confident. It helps to consider yourself an interesting person worthy of getting to know too. Today's activity will take you step-by-step through how to do this.

Then, ask yourself:

"What changes would I need to make to my thinking so that I look forward to every meeting with other people?"

And finally

"How will I do this?"

Successful interactions start with feeling good about 'you'

Successful interactions can only come about when you're feeling good about yourself. This is the reason I saved this chapter until the end. I wanted to get you recognising the amazing person you are ready to be a positive influence in the lives of others.

The activity that will follow begins with *Recognising the Positive You* activity (Chapter 3, Day 1) to get you feeling good. Once you have this good feeling, then continue with today's task which will get you in the mindset that you are socially confident. And the more you think in this way, the more you will become the socially successful person you desire to be.

👍 **THINK YOURSELF SOCIALLY SUCCESSFUL**

Preparing your mind for social confidence

1 Recall how you felt when doing the *Recognising the Positive You* activity (Chapter 3, Day 1). Remember all the good things about you and your positive qualities.

Mastering a socially confident mindset

2 Before every interaction with others today (and for the rest of the week), say to yourself, *"I enjoy interacting with others."* Let yourself smile as you do this!

- The phrase must sound positive and enthusiastic so you really look forward to all interactions.

- Imagine every conversation is enjoyable like talking with a good friend – comfortable, positive, uplifting, engaging.

You can enhance the success of this activity by revisiting the *Think Yourself Assertive* activity from Chapter 3, Day 5. As you become more socially confident you will find it easier to approach people and more comfortable to keep good conversations flowing. One of the many benefits of doing this is that more opportunities will become available to you – which will boost your social success even more!

Day 2: Listen for success

Being a good listener will make you seem instantly more interesting and attractive to others. I remember meeting somebody on a journey, listening to their interesting stories and worries. I found that I only had to add an occasional 'uh huh' or ask a question and that kept the conversation flowing. By the end of the journey he told me that I was so easy to talk to, and he was so grateful that I took the time to listen. And to achieve this, I didn't really have to speak that much. Instead I needed to listen and really understand the situation from his viewpoint. To do this, you don't necessarily have to agree with the other person's view, just understand it from their perspective.

Put on your listening ears

To be an effective hypnotherapist I need good listening skills. Quite often we are so keen to share our view and to give advice that we forget the ratio of 2 ears to 1 mouth. You should aim to listen for twice as long as you spend talking and pause occasionally to really listen to the other person.

Whilst listening might seem a basic skill, do you ever notice that you sometimes 'switch off' or think about other things when people are talking to you? Perhaps thinking about what you are going to have for dinner that night, the next question you will ask them, or thoughts about how you would have responded in their situation? To just listen is not as easy as you think.

And of course, I'm sure we all know somebody that likes to talk more than they listen? Long-term it doesn't make for such lasting relationships.

Being heard makes us feel valued and important

When you really listen with interest to someone, it makes them feel valued. By doing this they are more likely to open up to you and be honest as they can talk freely without being judged. To test this, think of a time when someone really listened to you. What was it like to feel understood and have someone give their time just to be there?

Use your two ears to best effect

I've designed today's activity to get you to become a really good listener. Even if you already are good at listening, it can be useful to do this from time-to-time, as it will help you to appreciate the views of others. You are also likely to find it will win you points with friends, family members or even colleagues!

👆 LISTEN EFFECTIVELY

1 *Look forward to being with others.* Before each conversation, get yourself in the right frame of mind by reminding yourself *"I enjoy interacting with others"* (Chapter 4, Day 1).

2 *Remove distractions.* That way you truly listen to the person you are communicating with. For instance, switch off the TV or stop what you're doing and listen.

3 *Give your full attention to the person who is speaking.* Avoid thinking of anything else and concentrate fully on what the person is saying.

4 *Notice any emotions of the other person.* This will help you to understand how they feel about what they're saying. For instance if they raise their voice, it many indicate frustration.

5 *Check your understanding.* Ask open questions that start with Who, What, Where, Why, When, How, Tell me about. Asking questions keeps the conversation going. It may also help to paraphrase by repeating back what has been said in your own words, or by briefly summarising the discussion. This demonstrates very strongly that you are listening too.

Whilst listening effectively is good practice for every situation, today and during this week consciously use this technique for two or three conversations that you have throughout the day. Try this not just during face-to-face conversations but when you're on the telephone too.

Day 3: Speak up for success

Why is it that starting conversations, particularly in certain social situations, can seem a real challenge? Take for example the networking setting. As you arrive, you realise that you don't know anyone at the meeting. There are people already in groups networking with ease with the conversation flowing naturally and effortlessly.

Imagine the conversation flowing with ease

How easy or awkward situations may seems depends on how you view them. If you enjoy the interaction of meeting new people and looking forward to finding out about others, then you are likely to ask lots of interesting questions and the conversation will flow easily. On the other hand, if you expect to run out of things to say and feel awkward, then that is what's likely to happen.

"But how can I overcome this and increase my social confidence?"

Successful conversations

There are some good tips I will share with you that will make speaking with people easier and a more comfortable process. Whether this is meeting new people, or enjoying conversations with friends, colleagues or even your boss!

The activity for today will be in two parts. The first part will take you through various techniques to improve your success when speaking with others. This includes ways to keep the conversation flowing effortlessly as well some tips to make people eager to listen to what you have to say.

The second part is about how to use your voice to build rapport. This is very powerful as when we feel that people are like us, and understand us, we are much more likely to open up. This makes for successful conversations which in turn can lead to more successful relationships.

👍 SUCCESSFUL CONVERSATIONS: PART 1

Use these tips to get people eager to listen to you

1 *Project your voice with confidence.* You will already have started to speak more confidently and assertively following the *Speaking with Confidence* activity from Chapter 3, Day 4. Read it again before continuing with the first part of today's activity.

2 *Be positive and interesting.* People are more likely to listen to your ideas if you are optimistic. Use appropriate enthusiasm to make yourself instantly more interesting.

3 *Approach every conversation with a positive mindset.* Avoid gossiping or complaining. If you do need to talk about something that's negative, such as if you disagree with someone's idea, then make sure you are constructive. For instance say why you disagree and offer alternative suggestions. Make it clear you are rejecting the idea and not the person.

4 *Listen Effectively* (Chapter 4, Day 2). For a successful conversation listen at least twice as much as you speak. ➲

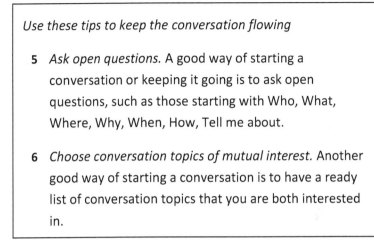

Use these tips to keep the conversation flowing

5 *Ask open questions.* A good way of starting a conversation or keeping it going is to ask open questions, such as those starting with Who, What, Where, Why, When, How, Tell me about.

6 *Choose conversation topics of mutual interest.* Another good way of starting a conversation is to have a ready list of conversation topics that you are both interested in.

Establishing successful conversations using rapport

After effective listening, your voice is one of the most powerful tools you have for establishing connections. The way to build rapport is to match some of the characteristics of the person you are speaking with. By doing this they are much more likely to feel valued and to listen to what you are saying. Here's how to establish rapport using your voice.

👍 **SUCCESSFUL CONVERSATIONS: PART 2**

1 *Listen.* Whenever you talk with someone get into the habit of listening to the qualities of their voice. For instance, listen for their:

   • *Pace.* Do they talk fast, or very s-l-o-w-l-y?

   • *Volume.* How do they project their voice?

   • *Choice of words.* When talking, people tend to emphasise words that have meaning for them. If you use the same words when responding, you're more likely to have a successful conversation.

   • *Tone.* Match the tone if appropriate.

2 *Match.* Now adapt the qualities of your voice so they are more in line with the person you are communicating with. Take care not to exactly mimic their voice as this may come across as patronising so breaking rapport.

   • If communicating with someone who is quite frustrated, match it initially and then gradually alter the qualities of your voice to be more calming.

Combining an enthusiastic approach that gets people eager to hear what you have to say, with rapport and effective listening, will add enormously to your social success. The best thing about doing this is that you will gradually start to enjoy talking more with others. As you relax into conversations and have fun practising these skills, you will start to become more appealing to others. A great boost to your social and personal confidence!

Day 4: Mindful interactions

We all like to feel important and valued by other people. Isn't it nice when someone takes the time and cares enough to show a genuine interest in you and really listens, asking nothing in return? If you could make each person you meet feel this good, then this would make for much more enjoyable interactions. This method of establishing rapport can be done by taking a genuine interest in the other person and what they have to say.

For me, I particularly enjoy speaking with people that seem to be on the same 'wavelength' as me. They seem to understand or even share a similar view – it makes it seem that we are somehow alike.

We are more comfortable with people who are like us

When people seem similar to us, particularly on an emotional level, it creates a powerful rapport. Establishing a trust and rapport is a proven way to improve social interactions and draw people to you. The following activity can be used in any interaction, whether with friends, family, partner or even business colleagues. I've personally found it to be a very powerful way of making genuine connections – and best of all, I find by using this technique that I really enjoy, and look forward to, social interactions.

👍 **MINDFUL INTERACTIONS**

Preparing your mind for social success

Before every interaction with others:

1 Take a few calming breaths (See the *1-Minute Breathe in Calm* activity from Chapter 1, Day 1).

2 So that your interactions are more successful, before every one say to yourself, *"I enjoy making you feel valued,"* and experience how pleased you are at a successful outcome.

Take action towards social success

3 Before every interaction today and for the rest of the week
   • hear *"I enjoy making you feel valued."*
   • vividly picture and experience what it might be like to already have good rapport with each other (as if you're speaking with a really good friend).

Using this technique will enable you to naturally and comfortably make connections with anyone you choose. You can even combine this with the *Think Yourself Assertive* activity from Chapter 3, Day 5. Do this and you will be able to draw people to you. It will not only brighten up their day but make you feel good too!

Day 5: Instant rapport

Yesterday we talked about the importance of making others feel valued as a proven way to create an instant rapport. We focused on using the power of our minds to naturally steer us towards enjoyable and successful conversations by thinking to ourselves *"I enjoy making you feel valued."* Making others feel important to us is the secret to achieving true social success.

Imagine you already have a good rapport

I shared with you yesterday a technique that works well for me to establish rapport. I imagine that the person I am speaking with is a close friend and that I already get on really well with them. Imagining I've known them for a long time makes me really look forward to speaking with them. I also find that I naturally listen to them with interest, and encourage them to tell me more using open questions. This works well because we are more receptive to people who we trust and perceive are like us. In that moment we share the same view of the world. When you get on well with others it is naturally reflected in your body language too.

You can create an instant rapport by matching body language

Have you ever noticed how people who get on well together tend to reflect it in their body language? They may lean towards each other or 'mirror' each other's posture. For instance, when a person crosses their legs, the other person will do the same.

Throughout today, just observe the body language of people around you. Notice those who are getting on well and how their body language is similar.

You might notice too that, just as we practiced in Chapter 4, Day 3 (*Successful Conversations Part 2*), their tone of voice and speed are similar. This happens naturally in an attempt to be like each other. Whilst this does occur at an automatic level, it can, to some extent, also be learnt. Doing this will help you to build powerful connections.

Today's activity will get you to notice how you naturally build rapport with other people. I found I learnt a lot about what makes me get on well with others when I first did this. Start by practising with someone you enjoy spending time with. Once you are comfortable doing this you can use it to create powerful connections with anyone you choose.

👍 **INSTANT RAPPORT**

1 When you next meet up with someone you enjoy spending time with, use the following technique to become consciously aware of the how you naturally build rapport. Notice how you match:

- posture, body movements or gestures
- facial expressions
- head movements
- breathing rate
- energy level.

2 Choose one of the items from the following list and practice with a friend:

- *Posture or body movements.* Wait a few seconds then perform a similar gesture. For instance if your friend folds their arms, then you may fold your hands in your lap.

- *Gestures.* When it's your turn to talk, use the same gestures as your friend.

- *Face expressions.* Match the facial expression instantly to acknowledge their emotion. For instance, if they raise their eyebrows, then you instantly follow.

- *Head nods.* Nod instantly when they do to reflect agreement or to encourage your friend to continue speaking.

➲

- *Breathing rate.* Inhale and exhale just as they do to create a really deep rapport.
- *Energy levels.* Match the energy, passion and charisma of your friend.

3 Choose a different item each day this week to practice with a friend.

One word of warning with this technique – it really does work! Carried out correctly, it will help anyone you communicate with feel instantly comfortable and at ease with you. To get the best from this, combine it with the *Mindful Interactions* activity (Chapter 4, Day 4).

Day 6: Being socially successful

By now you will be well on your way to making a positive and lasting impression. As your popularity and circle of friends and colleagues starts to increase, you can enjoy the additional social and personal confidence that brings.

Today I have some exceptional hints and tips to perfect your new-found confidence. Make people feel special and you will instantly become someone to cherish. Here's how to do that:

- *Show a genuine interest and appreciation.* Remember something about them that you can ask about when you next meet will demonstrate that you've thought about them. Make them feel like the most important person in the room.

- *Make time.* Share experiences together and enjoy each other's company. If you want to develop a lasting relationship, make time to keep in regular contact. Take the time to talk to others too.

- *Listen with interest.* Always give your full attention and listen without judgement. Take an interest and really understand the world from their viewpoint.

- *Give genuine praise.* A proven way to receive more compliments is to genuinely give praise and celebrate the successes of others.

- *Be approachable.* Being friendly, loyal and approachable will get people flocking to spend time with you. I find a warm and genuine smile goes a long way to being approachable.

The following activity puts all these techniques into practice. I've included references to each of the activities we've covered so far to support you in developing your social confidence. Take care though, used correctly these techniques are very effective and will instantly attract people to you!

SOCIAL CONFIDENCE

Activity	Description	Review activity
Prepare your mindset.	• Get yourself into the mindset of confidently developing successful interactions by thinking to yourself, *"I enjoy interacting with others."*	• Chapter 4, Day 1: *Think Yourself Socially Successful.*
	• Boost your confidence.	• Chapter 2, Day 2: *Think your Body Fit and Healthy.* • Chapter 3, Day 5: *Think Yourself Assertive.*
	• Prepare mutually interesting topics of conversation.	• Chapter 4, Day 4: *Mindful Interactions.*
Be approachable and confident.	• A friendly smile, a confident relaxed open posture and a positive attitude is highly attractive to others.	• Chapter 1, Day 4: *How to Think Positive.* • Chapter 3, Day 1: *Recognising the Positive You.* • Chapter 3, Day 3: *Standing Tall and Walking with Confidence.*
	• Be noticed by making a good first impression by looking your best.	• Chapter 3, Day 7: *Perfect Appearance.*
	• If you feel nervous during any interaction take a few diaphragmatic calming breaths.	• Chapter 1, Day 1: *1-Minute Breathe in Calm.*

Activity	Description	Review activity
Make others feel special.	• Put others at ease and make them feel valued and welcome. • Remember something important to them to talk about.	• Chapter 4, Day 4: *Mindful Interactions.*
Use rapport.	• Imagine you already know them well and have good rapport. • Mirror key characteristics such as gestures, expressions, energy.	• Chapter 4, Day 5: *Instant Rapport.*
Listen with genuine interest.	• Give your full attention and listen to the words as well as emotions. • Listen without judgement or defensiveness. Even if you don't agree, it may be valid from their viewpoint.	• Chapter 4, Day 2: *Listen Effectively.*
Be interesting.	• Speak with enthusiasm and confidence.	• Chapter 3, Day 4: *Speaking with Confidence.*

You can apply these techniques to a range of situations and interactions whether work related, family related or even finding a partner. You are now well on your way to achieving social success.

Day 7: The rest of your life – Sum your success

We're almost at the end of our *28 Days to Change Your Life*. It's time to think back to all the changes you've made and how far you've come over the past few weeks. What changes are you particularly pleased with? What worked well for you? What areas need further work? What actions will you take to achieve a happier, healthier and more fulfilling life for yourself?

Before we go I have one final secret to share with you. The secret to unlocking your true potential. That is to change your thinking patterns so you focus your mind on what you want. This will help you to enjoy a stress-free, totally confident and healthy you in the long-term, so you can enjoy building satisfying and lasting relationships with others. You can achieve this by regularly picturing successful outcomes.

This activity will help you to visualise your successful future that starts now.

BACK TO THE START

1 Take a few deep breaths using the *1-Minute Breathe in Calm* (Chapter 1, Day 1).

2 To make the experience more compelling make some time to relax. Use the *5-Minute Power Relax* from Chapter 1, Day 5.

3 It can help to close your eyes so you can focus fully on enjoying this experience.

4 Picture yourself exactly as you choose to be – relaxed, confident, healthy, enjoying interactions with others.

5 Make the experience really vivid. Actually feel yourself achieving whatever you want in your life. Enjoy how this makes you feel. For instance, perhaps you might imagine how you:

- Deal calmly and confidently with any situation.
  - o Reflect on your good posture, your style and the way you look, how you respond assertively, your confident voice.

- Lead a healthy lifestyle. Taking regular activity and making fresh natural food choices.

- Eat with control. Listening to your body and eating mindfully. Stopping eating when you register the full signal.

- Recognise all your fabulous qualities and how truly amazing and important you are.

- Enjoy interacting with others, making instant connections so easily and comfortably.

6 When you're ready, open your eyes.

7 Keep this successful image in your mind. Retain those good feelings and practice this activity whenever you want to boost your success and happiness.

Congratulations! You have started to change your life and master success.

CHAPTER 4 SUMMARY

The aim of this chapter was to provide you with the essential ingredients you need to achieve social success. Whether you want to be a people magnet and instantly attract others to you; develop fulfilling and lasting relationships; or both, requires:

- having the right frame of mind (looking forward to meeting people), and

- having the right behaviours (knowing how to build rapport).

What is really important is that you are genuine. If you really care about the person you are with and genuinely interested in them, you will truly be successful in your communication. It is possible to learn to be more socially confident and we looked at techniques to boost social success, including:

Mind techniques for social success

- *Genuinely looking forward to all conversations and meetings.* Keep in mind the phrase, "I enjoy interacting with others."

- *Make people feel valued.* With everyone you meet keep in mind the phrase, "I enjoy making you feel valued."

- *Enjoy being with others.* Create an instant connection by treating each person you meet as someone to be valued and cherished just as you would a close friend. Show an interest by appreciating them and giving genuine praise.

Behaviours for social success

- *Your voice is a powerful communication tool.* Make your voice easy and enjoyable to listen to. Be enthusiastic about what you say.

- *Put on your listening ears.* Share a genuine interest in the other person and listen twice as much as you speak. Remember to give them your full attention. Empathise. Remember everyone likes to feel listened to and understood.

- *Keep the conversation flowing.* Open questions and thoughtfully chosen topics of mutual interest will naturally keep the conversation flowing effortlessly.

- *People who are successful at communication naturally build rapport.* When people get on well it is reflected in their body language.

- *We like people who are like us.* We feel more comfortable around people who we believe are just like us. Make your voice, gestures, body language and energy levels similar to the person you are speaking with.

- *Regularly visualise success.* See yourself just as you want to be, enjoying life and being happy, healthy and confident.

Congratulations!

Now you have mastered your mind, you can enjoy achieving social success.

One final task

Just before we finish it's time to find out how you got on. Turn to the next page to review your progress and how far you've come since starting this programme.

REVIEW YOUR PROGRESS 2

How did you get on?

I'd like you to think back to how you felt before you began this programme. Take a moment to notice the changes you've made or useful tips and tools you've picked up along the way. If you're feeling more relaxed, confident or even just more in control, you're off to a good start.

Your long-term success

Your chances of long-term success with this programme will greatly increase if you confidently use these proven techniques. To help you determine what you need to continue to do, answer the following three key questions for each of the four areas we've covered during this programme.

For each of the four areas we've covered, ask yourself:

1. Where am I now?

    Stress Busting: _____

    Body Health: _____

    Confidence: _____

    Relationships: _____

2. What do I need to do, or continue to do, to make this a habit?

    Stress Busting: _____

    Body Health: _____

    Confidence: _____

    Relationships: _____

3. How and when will I achieve this?

Stress Busting:
_____

Body Health:
_____

Confidence:
_____

Relationships:
_____

Change starts by taking the first step

Write down the actions you will take. This is your commitment to yourself and your health and wellbeing. Create an action plan and make it as enticing and appealing as you can. That way you'll be able to enjoy more happiness, confidence and better health in the future.

To get you started I've prepared an example on the following page of how you can fit all these life enhancing techniques into even the most hectic schedule. You can adapt this planner to best fit your personal needs and lifestyle. What you will notice is that most activities should take no additional time over your existing routine. Instead it's about simply changing your habits to include these new tools.

If you already take regular physical exercise then to do all the activities in this book should take no more than an extra 15 minutes out of your day. Decide beforehand how you will schedule your time to make these changes that will enhance your health and wellbeing and get you looking and feeling great every day.

Activities Summary

How to fit these life enhancing activities into your busy life. Example only.
*These activities should take no (or minimal) additional time over your current routine

Time	Activity	Chapter/Day	When	Summary	Time (mins)	How to fit it into your day	Page
07:00	1-Minute breathe in calm	1/1	On waking	Practice calm breathing and set-up your positive mindset for the day	5	Set your alarm 5 minutes earlier than your current wake-up time	24
	Taking control of your thoughts	1/2					28
	How to think positive	1/4					36
	Who is the ideal you?	3/2					125
07:30	Perfect appearance	3/7	Get ready for the day	Get yourself looking and feeling your best	0*	While getting dressed	144
08:00	How to hydrate	2/7	During breakfast	Sip warm lemon water	0*	During breakfast	106

Time	Activity	Chapter/ Day	When	Summary	Time (mins)	How to fit it into your day	Page
08:00	Assessing hunger activity	2/3	During breakfast	Eat with control	0*	Think mindfully whilst eating	83
	Menu planner, Motivate yourself to make healthy food choices	2/4					87 & 90
	Your powerful guide to eating with control	2/5					95
	Reset your full signal	2/6					100
	How to become more mindful	1/3		Be mindful when eating			31
08:30	Standing tall and walking with confidence	3/3	Walk to work	Walk tall	0*	Becomes your normal walking style	129
	How to become more mindful	1/3		Be mindful when walking	0*	Think mindfully whilst walking	31
09:00	How to hydrate	2/7	Arrive at work	Fill your water bottle, remember to sip water during the day, and set reminders	0*	Have sufficient water available	106

Time	Activity	Chapter/Day	When	Summary	Time (mins)	How to fit it into your day	Page
09:00	1-minute breathe in calm	1/1	Through-out the day	During meetings, at your desk and when speaking with colleagues	0*	Good preparation for every interaction	24
	Think yourself assertive	3/5					136
	Speaking with confidence	3/4					132
	Instant assertiveness	3/6					141
	Think yourself socially successful	4/1					155
	Listen effectively	4/2					158
	Successful conversations (parts 1 & 2)	4/3					162 & 164
	Mindful interactions	4/4					167
	Instant rapport	4/5					171
	Social confidence	4/6					175
12:30	As 'during breakfast' activities	Various	During lunch	Eat with control, sip water, be mindful when eating	0*	Concentrate on eating	Various

Time	Activity	Chapter/ Day	When	Summary	Time (mins)	How to fit it into your day	Page
17:30	Keep active	2/1	At the gym/ during exercise	Keep fit and hydrated	60	Walk at lunch or set aside time in the evening	74
	Think your body fit and healthy	2/2		Whilst exercising			78
19:00	1-minute breathe in calm	1/1	When arriving home	5-minute power relax, including breathing, followed by positive thinking	10	As soon as you arrive home in the evening	24
	5-minute power relax	1/5					41
	Recognising the positive you	3/1					121
	Visualising your new stress-free life	1/7					54
	Back to the start	4/7					178
19:30	As 'during breakfast' activities	Various	During your evening meal	Eat with control, sip water or herbal tea, practice mindfulness during eating	0*	Be mindful whilst eating	Various
21:30	Sleep enhancing techniques	1/6	Begin 1-hour wind down before bedtime	Relaxing sleep routine	0*	Relax yourself at bedtime	50

Noticing the changes

As the saying goes, "all good things must come to an end." Now we've completed our 28 days together it's time for you to take charge. I hope you have enjoyed this programme and begun to make positive changes. I'd like you to take a moment to think back over techniques that worked particularly well for you and changes that you've made over the last few weeks. What worked best for you? And how can you easily include these new skills in your daily lifestyle?

How do I know if my mindset has been changed?

I'm confident that if you continue to follow the proven techniques you'll be amazed at how quickly your life changes for the better. You may already have begun to notice how you're using some of the techniques even without thinking about it. This is a positive sign that your mind has learnt new ways that work best for you. With a little practice, very soon many of these changes will become automatic and the preferred way for you.

Continuing the new ways

My aim was to inspire you to lead a healthy, happy life and by reflecting back on techniques that worked well for you I'm convinced you will notice a positive difference. I now encourage you to continue the good work as it will be well worth the investment in yourself.

Over to you

It is over to you now but if you would like further support with any of the techniques or to arrange a consultation, I have left the contact details of my clinic in the next section.

It has been a pleasure to support you on your new journey and until we next meet I wish you continued health, happiness and success.

Rachael

Meet Rachael Horton

Experienced Hypnotherapist and Biomedical Scientist

Renowned for her success in transforming lives Rachael Horton, experienced hypnotherapist, has helped hundreds of people eliminate stress, boost confidence and achieve personal success.

Author Photo: Dik Ng

Born and raised in Nottingham, Rachael studied biomedical science (gaining a First Class Degree), then gained a Diploma in Hypnotherapy before setting up the Change-4-Life Hypnotherapy Clinic.

Now based in the south east of England, Rachael has a successful and thriving hypnotherapy practice and is passionate about helping others make changes.

An established trainer and coach

Rachael frequently leads interactive and motivational training courses inspiring individuals to achieve their goals. If you would like to find out more about Rachael or her practice, please visit

www.change-4-life.com

A personal Thank You from the Author

As an author I consider myself part of a vast team, without which this book would never have come to print. This team includes not only those who have been instrumental in the publication of this book, but also all of those people I have worked with over the years.

To each of my clients, Thank You

I believe I have the most rewarding job in the entire world. I get to meet so many fascinating people on a daily basis who give me the opportunity to motivate and inspire them to achieve all the things they really want for themselves. To see them make incredible changes, often in a very short space of time, really is the most satisfying thing.

I would like to dedicate this book to all my clients from whom I have learnt so much. I have appreciated all the kind words and testimonials you have sent over the years. This has really meant a lot.

To those who have supported this book

I am personally indebted to all those talented and generous people who supported the development of this book. In particular to David Young – thank you so much for your patience and for taking the time to review and edit my proofs. I have learnt so much from you. Also Dik Ng for his superb photography and his friendly relaxed approach – I'm so thrilled with the result!; Ella Hart (www.cocos.co.uk) for the fantastic hair styling – you are very talented; Paul Dallibar who encouraged me to turn my ideas and experience into a book; and to Kim Fletcher, Lizzie Jeffery, Dee Blick and all those who trialled the book. Thank you for providing such valuable feedback that has made this book what it is today.

To my readers

Each activity in this book has been carefully selected and personally trialled and tested. I have thoroughly enjoyed writing this book with the purpose of improving your life. I hope you gained as much benefit and enjoyment out of it as I did writing it.

To my family

Finally, a book doesn't come together without the loving support of a good family. To my Mum, Dad, sister Karen and most of all Andrew Joyson. Thank you to you all for being just so fantastic. I couldn't ask for a better family.

Much love and thanks to you all.